Planetary Science

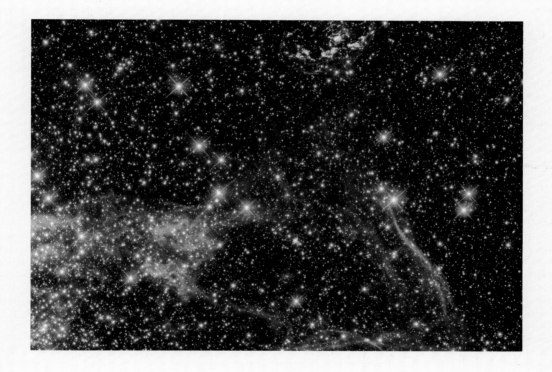

Developed at
The Lawrence Hall of Science,
University of California, Berkeley
Published and distributed by
Delta Education,
a member of the School Specialty Family

1558513
978-1-62571-784-9
Printing 1 — 9/2017
Webcrafters, Madison, WI

Table of Contents

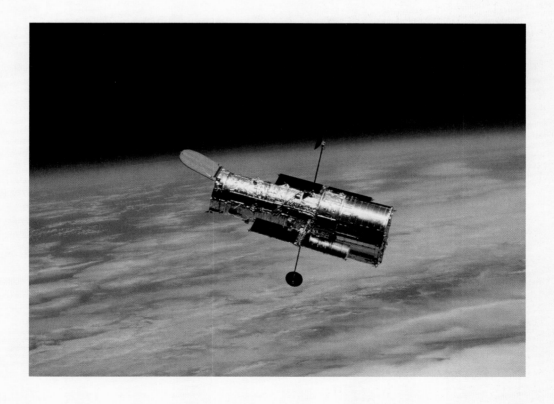

Sitting around this picnic table is a family system: a group of related, interacting people. Each person is not only part of a system, but also made up of systems: organ systems that work together to perform life functions.

Earth's Systems

You are an organism living on Earth. Your many functions include moving, seeing, hearing, eating, smelling, tasting, thinking, talking, and breathing.

Each function is managed by one or more of the organ **systems** of your body. These organ systems combine to form one large system—that system is *you*. A system is a collection of **interacting** parts. The parts work together to form a complex whole. If a system is made up of two or more smaller systems, those smaller systems are called **subsystems**.

The Human System

The human body includes multiple organ systems, such as the respiratory system and circulatory system. These subsystems interact to deliver oxygen to every cell in the body.

Planet Earth is a system, but it also is composed of subsystems that interact.

Do organ systems have subsystems? Yes. Each organ system consists of organs that work together, along with the fluids and gases they exchange. And organs have their own subsystems, made of tissues. Tissues have subsystems of cells that work together.

Are you part of a larger system? Yes, you are! As an inhabitant of Earth, you interact with many other organisms and natural materials. That means you are part of the grand system we call Earth.

Earth's Systems

Our **planet** Earth is a very large object, with many interacting parts. Like the human body, Earth is composed of subsystems. And like the human body, each Earth subsystem interacts with all the others.

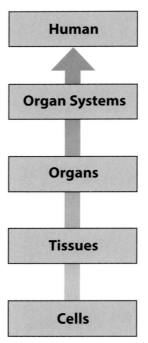

Each body system is made up of smaller subsystems that perform more and more specific functions. Each cell itself is a complex system.

Earth has a **core** made of iron and nickel. Around the core is a thick layer of rock called the **mantle**. The outside surface of Earth is covered by a thin, hard, rocky **crust**. The core, mantle, and crust are a system called the **geosphere**. But there is more to Earth than just the geosphere.

More than half of Earth is covered by water. Most of the water is in the ocean. A lot of water is in rivers, streams, lakes, ponds, and underground. And more water is stored in huge masses of ice near Earth's poles. Water is in the air as invisible water vapor and in droplets forming clouds and fog. The interacting water on, under, and above Earth's surface is a system called the **hydrosphere**.

Above Earth's surface is the **atmosphere**. The atmosphere is a system of interacting gases. Earth's crust, ocean, lakes, ponds, streams, and air are home to millions of plants, animals, fungi, and microorganisms. This is the **biosphere**. The biosphere is a system of interacting living organisms.

The atmosphere around Earth contains the gases we breathe and the clouds that are part of our weather.

Which systems can you find evidence of in this photo?

The huge Earth system is made of the geosphere, hydrosphere, atmosphere, and biosphere. Which of these Earth systems are humans a part of? As living organisms, we are part of the biosphere. But the answer is not so simple, because each Earth system affects the others.

System Interactions

How do Earth's systems interact? You breathe in oxygen and exhale carbon dioxide. You, as a member of the biosphere, are exchanging gases with the atmosphere. Look up and you might see clouds in the sky. This is the hydrosphere interacting with the atmosphere. Plants growing beside a river are an example of the biosphere interacting with the hydrosphere. On a larger scale, look at a dam on a river, built by humans to collect water for a city. The dam shows the biosphere interacting with the hydrosphere, and with the geosphere, which provided the materials for the dam.

Actions within the biosphere affect other Earth subsystems. The effects can go the other way, too. An earthquake or volcano (geosphere) can disrupt living organisms (biosphere). Later in this course, we will explore these interactions in more depth.

We will also look at Earth's place in the larger systems that are the **solar system**, **galaxy**, and **universe**. The universe is the largest system that we know of. It has many, many subsystems. Your **frame of reference** for your place within the **cosmos** can range from a cell and all its systems within an organism, to Earth and all its systems within the universe.

Think Questions

1. **How did you interact with Earth's systems on your way to school today?**
2. **Explain how changing your frame of reference can affect which systems you can observe.**

This concrete arch dam holds and produces electricity from 1.1 billion cubic meters of water, but this engineering marvel is not just about the hydrosphere.

The First Voyage of Columbus

Many people believe that Columbus wanted to prove that Earth is round. But Columbus already knew Earth is round. The question to answer was, how *big* is Earth?

During the time of Christopher Columbus (1451–1506), European traders made difficult journeys across thousands of miles of land. They traveled as far as China, India, Persia, Japan, and Southeast Asia. Europeans called this region the Indies and referred to it as the land of many riches. The riches that they searched for included spices, gold, and silk. Transporting these goods to Europe was costly because of the difficult journey.

Sailors aboard the *Pinta*, the fastest of Columbus's three ships, were the first to spy land on October 12, 1492. This replica is part of a museum in Brazil.

Columbus was the business agent for several important Italian families. He wanted to find a sea route to the Indies. Travel by sea could reduce the time and expense of transportation. Columbus would be able to sell the goods at a much higher profit.

Finding the Best Route

In 1488, the Portuguese captain Bartolomeu Dias (1450–1500) found an eastern route to the Indies. He sailed down the west coast of Africa, around the southern tip, and up its eastern coast to the Indies. But Columbus had a different plan. He wanted to sail west across the ocean to reach the Indies from the other side.

In Columbus's time, Europeans had no idea that North America, South America, Central America, and the Caribbean Islands existed. Europeans did not know how wide the ocean west of Portugal was.

Columbus was using a world map that looked like this. Can you see what is missing? The eastern sea route (red) took European traders around the stormy southern tip of Africa. Columbus wanted to try a new route (blue), which he thought would save time and money.

Columbus tried to convince the rulers of England and France to pay for his journey, but most said no. His plan was risky because it called for sailing west into unknown waters. When Columbus asked for funds from King Ferdinand (1452–1516) and Queen Isabella (1451–1504) of Spain, they listened. They sent him to Spain's best university to talk with scholars about his plan.

The Size of Earth

Columbus had seen islands appear to rise from the ocean as he sailed toward them. On a flat Earth, this would not happen. Scholars had known the Earth is round for more than 1,800 years.

So what did Columbus discuss with the scholars? It was not about the shape of Earth. It was about the size of Earth.

Columbus sailed westward from Spain into uncharted territory, confident of reaching land. Ten weeks later, he stepped ashore on a small island in modern-day Bahamas, which he named San Salvador.

Columbus thought that Earth was about 30,000 kilometers (km) around. The trip from Europe to the Indies using the eastern route was 19,000 km. Columbus reasoned that the distance across the ocean from Spain to the Indies is probably less than 9,500 km.

The scholars, however, argued that Earth is about 38,000 km around. They reasoned that the voyage west across the ocean to the Indies would be 19,000 km or more. Traveling that far would take about 3 months.

Three months was a problem. The ships of that time could store only enough food and water for a trip of about 1 month. The scholars argued that Columbus and his crew would die of thirst or starvation.

Early Models of Earth

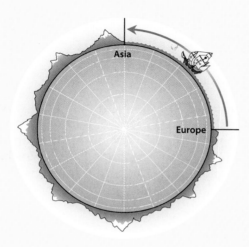

The world according to Columbus put Asia about one-quarter of the way around the globe.

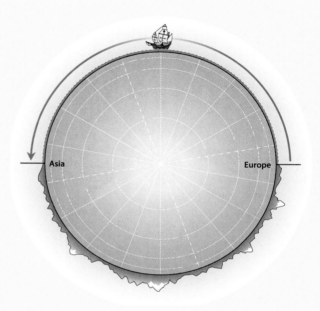

Scholars disagreed, calculating that the distance was twice as far.

Making the Trip

Columbus and his crew would be risking their lives to sail west across the ocean. King Ferdinand and Queen Isabella would be risking a lot of money from the Spanish treasury. Nevertheless, they finally agreed.

In 1492, Columbus and his crew set sail in three tiny boats, the *Niña*, the *Pinta*, and the *Santa Maria*. They sailed from southern Spain to the Canary Islands, at about **latitude** 28° north. Then they went straight across the ocean until they arrived at some islands about 2 months later.

Columbus believed that the islands were part of the East Indies. But a later explorer found that Columbus had landed in the "New World." The islands were part of the Bahamas, just off the southern tip of Florida. Columbus was lucky that the islands were there. If he had not struck land when he did, he and his crew would have died of thirst, as the scholars had predicted.

Modern Model of Earth

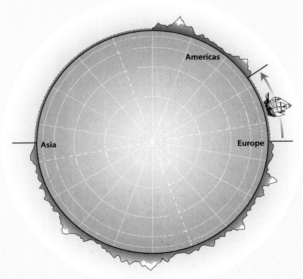

After sailing for 10 weeks, Columbus thought he had arrived in Asia, but it was actually the Americas.

Columbus's small fleet carried a total crew of 88 experienced seamen, and sailed on average 150 km a day. The flagship *Santa Maria* held most of the provisions, which were dangerously low when the expedition finally made landfall.

"Discovering" America

So did Columbus discover America? He *did* land in the Americas, but by accident. He was headed for Asia, but instead landed on a different continent. And there is evidence that other explorers arrived there much earlier.

Around 2,800 years ago, African traders might have sailed to present-day southeastern Mexico. Around 455 AD, the Chinese Buddhist priest Hui Shan is reported to have sailed across the Pacific Ocean to the Americas. He called the land Fusang. Polynesian explorers might have reached

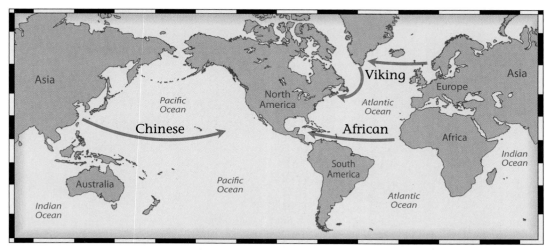

There is evidence that African, Chinese, and Viking explorers preceded Columbus's journey to the Americas.

Columbus visited five islands in the Bahamas before reaching what he assumed was China—actually Cuba. Even the first tiny islet, which he named San Salvador, was home to native peoples.

South America around 600 years ago. There is also evidence that the Viking explorer Bjarni Herjólfsson (960–1022) visited North America in the summer of 986. He was followed soon after by another Viking, Leif Eriksson (970–1020).

But in fact, the Americas were not discovered by any of these people. All the explorers who reached North America, Central America, South America, and the Caribbean Islands found native peoples who had been living there for thousands of years.

Think Questions

1. **Columbus sailed to the Canary Islands, at latitude 28° north, and then headed west. Eventually, he landed in the Americas. How do you think Columbus was able to cross the ocean without wandering north or south by accident?**

2. **When Columbus arrived in the Caribbean, people were living on the islands he "discovered." So who do you think discovered America?**

Seasons on Earth

What do you imagine when you read these words: summer, spring, fall, winter?

Most of us come up with a mental picture or two. Summer means shorts and T-shirts, swimming, and fresh fruits and vegetables. Winter means heavy coats and short days, perhaps with a blanket of snow on everything.

Seasons are pretty easy to tell apart in most parts of the United States. The amount of daylight, the average temperature, and the behavior of plants and animals are some indicators of the season. But do seasons change over time? What have you learned in class about the reasons for the seasons?

Even without a calendar, you can tell that this photograph was taken in autumn. The colorful leaves, responding to changes in light and temperature, are a clue to the season.

Earth's Motion

Here is a quick review of basic information about Earth's motion. Earth spins on an imaginary axle called an **axis**. The axis passes through the North and South Poles. Spinning on an axis is called **rotation**. It takes 24 hours for Earth to make one complete rotation.

Earth travels around (**orbits**) the **Sun**. Traveling around something is called **revolution**. Earth's orbit around the Sun is not exactly round. It is slightly oval. One revolution takes 365.25 days, which we call 1 year.

Take Note

Record the reasons for seasons on Earth. You can add more after reading this article, but record your first ideas now.

Earth's motion in space—rotation on its axis and revolution around the Sun—cause the daily cycle of day and night and the yearly cycle of the seasons. (This illustration is not drawn to scale.)

The average distance between the Sun and Earth is about 150 million kilometers (km). Earth's orbit is slightly oval, so Earth is sometimes farther away from and sometimes closer to the Sun. This distance is so insignificant that it is not related to the seasons.

It would seem logical that summer would be when Earth is closest to the Sun. That idea is wrong. Each year when Earth is closest to the Sun, the Northern Hemisphere experiences winter.

Earth's Tilt

Earth is not straight up and down on its axis as it revolves around the Sun. It is tilted at a 23.5° angle. The reasons for the seasons are linked to Earth's tilt.

Think about Earth revolving around the Sun. As Earth revolves, it also rotates on its axis. One rotation takes 24 hours. Throughout its rotation and revolution, Earth's North Pole always points toward the **North Star**, no matter where Earth is.

Tilt Equals Season

Look at the diagram that shows Earth in its orbit around the Sun. Notice that the North Pole points toward the North Star in all four seasons.

Study the summer **solstice** position of Earth. Because of the tilt, the North Pole is "leaning" toward the Sun. When the North Pole is leaning toward the Sun, daylight is longer. The angle at which light hits that part of Earth is around 90 degrees. Both of these factors result in more **solar energy** falling on the Northern Hemisphere. It is summer even though Earth is actually farther from the Sun. And when it is summer in the Northern Hemisphere, it is winter in the Southern Hemisphere.

Take Note

Is Earth closer to the Sun in winter or in summer? Is distance from the Sun a reason for seasons on Earth? Answer these questions in your notebook.

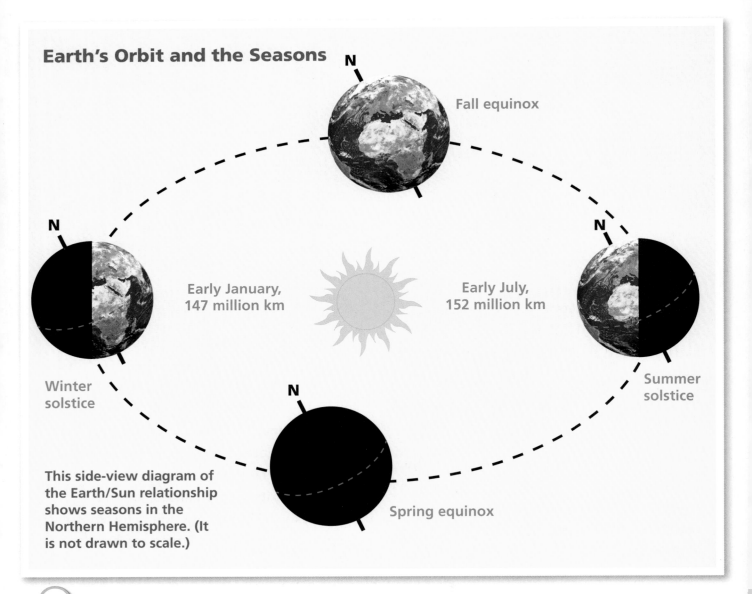

Earth's Orbit and the Seasons

Fall equinox

Early January, 147 million km

Early July, 152 million km

Winter solstice

Summer solstice

Spring equinox

This side-view diagram of the Earth/Sun relationship shows seasons in the Northern Hemisphere. (It is not drawn to scale.)

Look at the position of Earth 6 months later (at winter solstice). Now the opposite is true. Even though Earth is closer to the Sun at this time, the Northern Hemisphere is leaning away from the Sun. Daylight hours are shorter, and sunlight hits the Northern Hemisphere at a lower solar angle, so it gets less solar energy. It is winter in the Northern Hemisphere.

Four days in the year have names based on Earth's **location** around the Sun. In the Northern Hemisphere, summer solstice is June 21 or 22, when the North Pole tilts toward the Sun. Winter solstice is December 21 or 22, when the North Pole tilts away from the Sun.

In the Northern Hemisphere on the winter solstice, there are areas of Earth where the light from the Sun never reaches. People gather nearby to watch the Sun rise and set, barely peeking over the horizon.

The 2 days when the Sun's rays shine straight down on the **equator** are the **equinoxes**. On these 2 days, Earth's axis is tilted neither away from nor toward the Sun. *Equinox* means "equal night." Daylight and darkness are equal (or nearly equal) all over Earth. The spring (also called vernal) equinox is in March. The fall (also called autumnal) equinox is in September.

Day Length

We take day and night for granted. They always happen. Earth rotates on its axis, and the Sun appears to rise. Then the Sun appears to set. This cycle started long before humans appeared on Earth. It will most likely continue for millions of years.

Every day, the Sun appears to rise in the east, move across the sky, and set in the west. The length of daylight varies, though, depending on the time of year.

Because Earth is tilted, the length of day and night for any one place on Earth changes as the year passes. This table shows how hours of daylight change at different latitudes during the year. When it is summer in the Northern Hemisphere, the North Pole tilts toward the Sun. During summer at the North Pole, the Sun never sets. Above the Arctic Circle (latitude 66.5° north), daylight can last up to 24 hours in the summer. Night can last up to 24 hours during the winter.

Think Questions

Turn to your notebook entry about the reasons for the seasons that you made at the beginning of this article. What do you need to add? What do you need to change?

Length of Daylight in the Northern Hemisphere

Latitude	Summer solstice	Winter solstice	Equinoxes
0° N	12 hr.	12 hr.	12 hr.
10° N	12 hr. 35 min.	11 hr. 25 min.	12 hr.
20° N	13 hr. 12 min.	10 hr. 48 min.	12 hr.
30° N	13 hr. 56 min.	10 hr. 4 min.	12 hr.
40° N	14 hr. 52 min.	9 hr. 8 min.	12 hr.
50° N	16 hr. 18 min.	7 hr. 42 min.	12 hr.
60° N	18 hr. 27 min.	5 hr. 33 min.	12 hr.
70° N	24 hr.	0 hr.	12 hr.
80° N	24 hr.	0 hr.	12 hr.
90° N	24 hr.	0 hr.	12 hr.

Eratosthenes: First to Measure Earth

Stand in the middle of a field and look around. The field looks flat, so you might infer that Earth is flat. How could you find evidence that Earth is round?

More than 2,000 years ago, the Greek librarian and mathematician Eratosthenes (air•uh•TOSS•then•eze; about 276–196 BCE) heard a story that interested him. In the city of Syene, Egypt, on the Nile River, the Sun shone directly down an abandoned well at noon on June 21. Only then could one see the dry bottom. This simple observation started Eratosthenes thinking. For that story to be true, the Sun would have to be directly over the well. At the same time, he reasoned, a perfectly straight pole standing next to the well would not have any shadow at all.

Seen from space, Earth is obviously round. Early scientists did not have that vantage-point advantage, and yet they calculated not only the shape but also the size of our planet.

Going beyond the Story

Eratosthenes believed that the Sun is very far from Earth. From that distance, a beam of light reaching Earth would be **parallel** to every other beam of light reaching Earth. What would happen if Earth were flat? The Sun would be directly overhead everywhere while it was directly over the dry well. Furthermore, poles standing perfectly straight in the ground anywhere on Earth would cast no shadow at that time.

And what would happen if Earth were round? Eratosthenes reasoned that poles standing perfectly straight in the ground would be shadowless in a very small area. Poles would have shadows everywhere else.

Comparison of Earth Models

N   S

N   Shadow   Shadow   S

Shadows cast on a flat surface differ from those on a curved surface.

Eratosthenes discovered that poles outside the city of Syene did cast shadows at noon on June 21. The farther north they were, the longer the shadows. This discovery was evidence of a round Earth.

Shadow Evidence of Round Earth

The varying length of noontime shadows at different places proved Earth was not flat.

An Experiment

Eratosthenes tried an experiment based on his observations. He and a friend arranged to observe the shadows cast by identical poles, placed in different locations, at exactly the same time (noon) on June 21. In Syene, the pole next to the well cast no shadow. The Sun's rays were parallel to the pole. But in Alexandria, 800 kilometers (km) to the north, a pole cast a shadow. Eratosthenes reasoned that the pole in Alexandria was at a different angle than the incoming rays of light from the Sun. Because both poles were perfectly straight up and down, the surface of the land must be at a different angle, as on a curved surface.

The position of the Sun in the sky depends on time of day and latitude. The lower the Sun, the longer the shadows.

Doing the Math

Eratosthenes used the length of the shadow in Alexandria, geometry, and a protractor to determine that the Sun shone on the city of Alexandria at an angle of 7.2° (1).

Eratosthenes also knew that distance around an arc (circle) can be described in degrees. A complete circle is 360°. One-half of a circle is 180°. And one-fourth of a circle is 90° (2).

Eratosthenes wanted to know what part of a circle 7.2° is. Using the same reasoning, he divided 7.2° by 360° and got 1/50. Eratosthenes then measured the distance from Syene to Alexandria. He used a standard unit, called the stadium. He found that the two cities were 5,000 stadia apart. So 5,000 stadia was 1/50 of the distance around the circle that is the **circumference** of Earth. He then multiplied 5,000 by 50. He found that Earth is 250,000 stadia in circumference (3).

Applying Geometry to Calculate Earth's Size

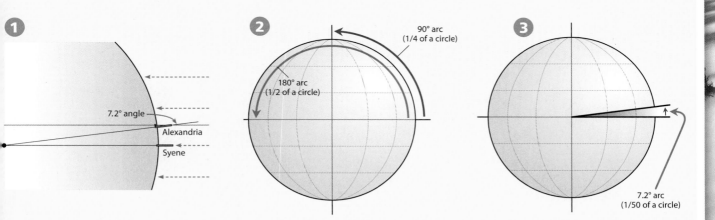

Eratosthenes measured the solar angle difference between Alexandria and Syene (7.2°) and realized that was 1/50 of a circle. He also knew the distance between the cities. So he multiplied that distance by 50 to estimate the size of Earth.

How Accurate

Eratosthenes' investigation involved simple science, math, and creative thinking. Because no one today knows for sure how long a stadium was, it is difficult to argue with the result Eratosthenes calculated. Using a likely value for the stadium of 185 meters (m), modern scholars come up with an estimate of 46,250 km for Eratosthenes's circumference of Earth. That is a pretty good estimate. Today's accepted circumference is 40,074 km.

Today, there is no question about the shape of Earth. We have seen images taken from space, and Earth is round. But think for a moment about the accomplishment of Eratosthenes. More than 2,000 years ago, he measured Earth with some shadows and a protractor.

Think Questions

1. **Why do you think Eratosthenes selected June 21 for his observations?**
2. **What might a shadow look like from a pole placed 400 km north of Syene at noon on June 21?**

Even with modern space technology, scientists use mathematics and models to investigate objects too large or too far away to measure directly.

Lunar Myths

Rona in the Moon

One bright evening, Rona went to fetch water from the stream for her children. In her hand was a basket containing a calabash (a hollow, dry gourd) to hold the water. While she was on her way, the **Moon** suddenly disappeared behind a cloud. On the narrow path lined with trees and bushes, she stumbled on a root. In her momentary anger, she cursed the Moon, saying, "You cooked-headed Moon, not to come forth and shine!"

These words displeased the Moon, who came down to Earth and took Rona. Rona caught hold of a ngaio tree that was growing on the bank of the stream. The Moon tore the tree up by the roots and flew away, taking Rona, the tree, and the calabash in the basket far up into the sky. Her friends and children, thinking she was away a long time, went to look for her. Not finding any traces of her, they called, "Rona, O Rona, where are you?" She answered from the sky, "Here I am, mounting aloft with the Moon and **stars**."

When it is a clear night, especially when the Moon is full, Rona may be seen reclining against the rocks, her calabash at her side, and the ngaio tree close by.

Myth from the Maori people of New Zealand. From Myths and Legends of the Polynesians by Johannes C. Andersen (New York: Dover, 1995).

Think Questions

1. **What does this myth describe about the Moon?**
2. **Why do so many cultures have myths about the Moon?**

According to the Maori Moon legend, when Rona upsets her calabash, or water-filled gourd, it rains.

The South American Yasi myth was a way to explain the phases of the Moon.

Father Moon

Yasi had a son. One day, the boy was playing with a jaguar and was accidentally killed. The jaguar was terrified and ran deep into the forest to hide forever. Yasi wanted to find out who the killer was, but none of the animals would tell him. This so enraged Yasi that he gave the howler monkey a long neck, put spines on the porcupine, and put the tortoise in a heavy shell.

Yasi was still furious, so he leaped up into the night sky to search for his son's killer. He searched all across the land and the sky. Each day, Yasi got dirtier and dirtier until he was completely covered with soil and leaves. He stopped by a stream to rest and clean himself. Each day as he rested, Yasi washed a little bit of his face. Finally, he was completely rested and clean. He resumed the search for his son's killer.

Yasi is still wandering the skies today. He spends half his time hunting and half his time resting. When he returns from the hunt, his face is completely covered in dirt. He washes off a little of the dirt each day until his face shines brightly once again.

Myth from the Siriono people of eastern Bolivia.

Moon and His Sister

Moon was a good-spirited and friendly Native American whose face was even brighter than that of the Sun. Moon had one sister, a small star who was often seen beside him. He had many other star friends.

One day Moon gathered all his friends together for a great feast. His house was very small. Soon the guests had taken up all the space.

As soon as Moon's sister arrived, Moon asked her to fetch water for him in several buckets. This was not an easy task, as it was winter. She had to fight with the cold, howling wind as she walked to get the water. The water was frozen by the river. She had to chip through the ice to fill the buckets.

She walked back to the house with her heavy burden, only to find that there was no room inside for her. She called to her brother, "Where can I sit?"

Moon was in a very good mood, and he just grinned at his sister. "There isn't enough space for even a mouse in here. I guess you will have to sit on my shoulder," he laughed.

Moon's little sister was not in the mood for his good humor. She took him at his word and jumped onto his shoulder. There she sits even today, holding on to her water buckets. Moon is not as bright as he once was because the shadow from her buckets dims his face.

Myth from the Native Americans of the northwest coast of North America.

When you look at the Moon, can you see shadows on its face, as Native Americans describe in this story?

Tale of the Rabbit

There were four Suns in previous ages, and all had ended in destruction. The gods came together to create a new and final Sun. To create the Sun, one of the gods would have to jump into the fire, the hearth of the gods. The gods gathered at the hearth at midnight to determine which god would make the sacrifice and become the Sun.

Two gods volunteered. One of them was wealthy and strong, the arrogant Tecciztécatl. The other god was poor and sick, the frail Nanahuatzin. Both agreed to die in order to raise the new Sun.

But when the strong god approached the fire, the flames flared high. He drew back from the edge, frightened. His fellow gods shouted encouragements to him to take the leap, but he could not.

Humble Nanahuatzin approached the fire. Without hesitating, he leaped into the flames. His body sizzled, crackled, and burned. This gave Tecciztécatl the courage to jump, and he did. The other gods waited in the darkness for signs of the dawn and Nanahuatzin's transformation into the fifth Sun.

The Aztec creation story says that dark shapes on the face of the Moon were formed by a rabbit thrown against it to dim its light.

The gods kept arguing among themselves as to where the Sun would first appear. Each one stood looking in a different direction, so that they would be sure to see the Sun as it first came up. Finally, the Sun appeared brilliant and red in the east, the direction of creation and new life. Following the Sun, Nanahuatzin, was a second very bright ball, Tecciztécatl, reincarnated as the Moon. Both balls remained still. To get them to move across the sky, the rest of the gods had to sacrifice themselves in the fire.

But before they died, one of the gods did something to the Moon. He grabbed a rabbit and hurled it into the Moon's bright face, darkening it tremendously. You can still see the imprint of the rabbit on the face of the Moon today.

Myth from the Aztecs of Mexico.

Many myths explain the relationship between the Sun and the Moon, the two celestial objects most visible from Earth.

Bahloo, Moon Man

Bahloo, the Moon, was lonely high up in the empty sky. He decided to visit Earth. When the campfires were burning and the girls were dancing, Bahloo came down close to Earth and lowered his shining face to speak to the girls. They were frightened by this bright, round white thing and ran away.

The next night he returned to find two other girls sitting on the riverbank. "How beautiful the moonlight is," sighed one of the girls. This was encouraging to Bahloo, and he decided to come closer to the girls. He broke into a run, puffing and blowing, his big belly shaking. The girls were surprised by Bahloo. They didn't know whether to laugh or shout for help. They ran a safe distance away and stood there staring back at the Moon.

To Australian Aborigines, the monthly cycle of waxing and waning reflects the Moon Man's alternating boldness and shyness.

Bahloo's feelings were hurt. He sat down by the riverbank and cried. The girls felt sorry for Bahloo and returned. They invited him to ride in their canoe to the other side of the river. But Bahloo was so big that, when he stepped into the canoe, it rocked and tipped, and then turned over, dumping Bahloo into the water. The round shining Moon sank down, down into the water. His light became dimmer and dimmer. The girls laughed and ran home.

Bahloo was very embarrassed. He climbed into the sky without anyone noticing. He remained hidden for several days. Gradually, he regained his courage and grew round and bright for all to see. But when he remembered the girls and how they laughed at him, he began to get smaller and soon went out of sight. Every month, Bahloo grows round and bright and full of courage, and every month he remembers his fall into the river and shrinks away to hide.

Myth from the Aborigines of Australia.

For thousands of years, cultures around the world have developed myths about the Moon. The full Moon has especially fascinated people from ancient times to today.

Observing the predictable patterns of movement of the Sun was the earliest way to record and anticipate the passage of time.

Measuring Time with Calendars

How would life change if there were no calendars? How would you celebrate your birthday if you did not know when it was?

What did people do before they had calendars to keep track of important days and events that were coming up?

Calendars help us keep track of passing time. They help us plan for the future. Long before people developed calendars, they observed nature to mark time. The day is one obvious way to measure time. Counting days, sunrise to sunrise, helps us keep track of events in the past (such as 10 days ago) and think about events in the future (such as 3 days from now).

The month-long lunar cycle was one way people measured time in the past. *Month* and *moon* are both derived from the same root word, *mensis*, because their meaning was so closely tied together.

Long ago, people noticed that the time between sunrise and sunset is not always the same. Observers in the Northern Hemisphere determined that one day each year is shorter than all the others. That day is the winter solstice. It marks the first day of winter. Then days get longer and longer until the longest day of the year, the summer solstice. Days then get shorter until the winter solstice returns. The time from one winter solstice to the next is 365.25 days, or 1 year.

The Moon

People also measured time with Moon observations. Over time, shepherds and other observers saw the repeating pattern of Moon **phases**. When you tally the days from one **full Moon** to the next, the cycle is always 29 or 30 days. The unit of time from one full Moon to the next is 1 **lunar** month.

Did You Know?

If you keep track of the number of lunar months from one winter solstice until the next, you would count approximately 12 lunar months, that is, 354 days. This is called a lunar year.

Lunar Year and Solar Year

Early calendars most often used lunar cycles. However, the lunar year does not exactly match the **solar** year. A solar year can be measured exactly from one winter solstice to the next winter solstice. In a lunar year, the winter solstice lands on a different date every year. The lunar year is about 11 days shorter than the solar year. This mismatch has been a problem for calendar makers.

The Modern Calendar

The calendar that we use today started off by following the patterns of the Moon.

In an early version of our calendar, each month began with the sighting of the new **crescent Moon**. More than 2,000 years ago, the Roman Empire decided not to match the calendar each month with the Moon. All months except February were assigned either 30 or 31 days, and the official year was 365 days long.

This 365-day calendar is the Gregorian calendar. This solar calendar accurately predicts annual events like the solstices. The solar calendar depends on Earth's position in its orbit around the Sun. Most of the world uses it for official business.

However, many people use different calendars for religious observances and traditional celebrations. For example, Rosh Hashanah (Jewish), Ramadan (Muslim), Diwali (Hindu), Easter (Christian), and Chinese New Year do not occur on the same date every year. All these holidays rely on calendars that connect to the lunar cycle. Some calendars follow both solar and lunar cycles.

A Sample of Calendars Used around the World			
Type of calendar	Lunar	Solar	Lunisolar
Chinese			X
Gregorian		X	
Hindu			X
Islamic	X		
Jewish			X
Persian		X	

The most widely used calendar in the world today, whether displayed on your wall, desk, monitor, or smartphone, is the Gregorian. It was introduced in 1582 to standardize time throughout Europe.

While our calendar began by reflecting the patterns of nature, over time we have relied less and less on observing nature. Usually we look for the date on a calendar or a computer. The calendar system that we currently use was set more than 400 years ago. It will probably not change anytime soon.

Think Questions

1. In what ways does the modern calendar connect with nature?
2. Do you or anyone you know follow more than one calendar system? Which ones?
3. What is a leap year? When is it, and why do we have it?

Calculating the Observance of Ramadan

It is April 2020, and it is Ramadan. That means Hussein Malik and his family in Oakland, California, are preparing to fast.

The new crescent Moon marks the first day of each month on the Islamic calendar. The ninth month is Ramadan. During Ramadan, Muslims do not eat or drink from sunrise to sunset. This fasting helps Muslims focus on their religious practice.

Because the Islamic calendar is lunar, the months shift by about 11 days every year. During Ramadan in 2020, Hussein's family eat their first meal of the day after sunset, around 8:00 p.m. Hussein's mother remembers years when Ramadan started in the winter. In winter, fasting is a lot easier, because the Sun sets around 5:00 p.m. in the Northern Hemisphere.

Unlike the solar-based Gregorian calendar, the Islamic calendar—or Hijri—is a lunar calendar.

Observation versus Calculation

On April 26, 2020, a relative called to say that the crescent Moon was sighted in California. So Hussein's family started fasting that day. Hussein's cousins Bilal and Aisha live in Dallas, Texas. In Dallas, many people started fasting on April 24, 2 days earlier.

Bilal's and Aisha's community uses scientific calculations to determine the first day of Ramadan. People can predict Moon phases, as we have in class. Some Muslims use scientific predictions to signal the start of Ramadan. They no longer wait to see the crescent Moon. Astronomers determined that the crescent Moon was above the horizon for about 30 minutes in parts of North America on April 24. The scientists did not actually see the Moon. But their calculations told them that it was in the evening sky in Dallas.

The One True Date

So these two families observe the same religious event on different days. Which is the "true" date of Ramadan? For decades, Muslims in North America have debated that question. The traditional way relies on local observers to see the first crescent Moon. Those observers then announce the beginning of the month. Clouds can cover the Moon. Different parts of the world have different views of the sky as Earth rotates. Therefore, the month of Ramadan can start on different dates in different places.

But many Muslims now consider direct observation of the crescent Moon unnecessary. Calculations show precisely when Ramadan starts. They are based on Earth's rotation and the Moon's orbit. Using scientific calculations helps Muslims plan their time off from school or work for religious observances.

Old and New Calendars

Finding the start of Ramadan highlights the different ways we can mark time. On one hand, people have looked for the Moon to mark the new month for more than

Relying on actual sightings of the new Moon means that Muslims across the United States and the rest of the world, might begin observing Ramadan on different dates.

1,400 years. This method keeps people connected with the natural cycles of the Moon.

On the other hand, starting the month based on scientific calculations makes the calendar universal. A standardized calendar makes it easier to follow a schedule. It helps people prepare for the month.

The Muslim community and other cultures continue to discuss traditional versus modern methods of observation. Some Muslims use scientific observations of the Moon to inform their religious practice. Their beliefs do not disappear just because they are using science. People of many different religious beliefs use and study science every day.

Think Questions

1. Some people use photographic evidence to start Ramadan. Would you trust a photograph posted to a website as evidence to begin the month of Ramadan? Why or why not?

2. Imagine you had to decide for your family when to start and end Ramadan. Would you look for the Moon, or would you use scientific calculations to determine the new crescent Moon? Why would you choose that method?

Earth's Moon

The Moon shines so brightly in the sky that you can sometimes see it even during the day. But the Moon does not make its own light. The light you see coming from the Moon is reflected sunlight.

The Moon is a sphere. When light shines on a sphere, the sphere is half lit and half dark. It does not matter where you position the sphere. It is always half lit and half dark.

The same is true for the Moon. It is always half lit and half dark. The half that is lit is the side toward the Sun. The half that is dark is the side away from the Sun. Look at the diagram on the next page to think about where you are on Earth when you see the Moon during day or night.

The Moon is so bright that it can cast shadows at night or be seen in the daytime sky. But the Moon is a reflector, not a source, of light, so moonlight is really reflected light from the Sun.

Lunar Phases

The Moon does not always appear to be the same shape. That is because half of the Moon is always dark. The other half is lit by the Sun. As the Moon orbits Earth, observers on Earth see different amounts of the lit half. The different shapes of the Moon are called phases. The phases change in a regular pattern as the Moon orbits Earth. The Moon completes an orbit and goes through its cycle of phases in just over 4 weeks.

Four specific phases happen about 1 week apart. The **new Moon** is invisible to us. It occurs when the Moon is between Earth and the Sun, so we are looking at the dark side of the Moon. The full Moon occurs when Earth is between the Sun and the Moon, so we are looking at the lit side of the Moon. Halfway between the new Moon and the full Moon is the **first-quarter Moon**. We see it half lit and half dark. Halfway between the full Moon and the new Moon is the **third-quarter Moon**.

Day and Night

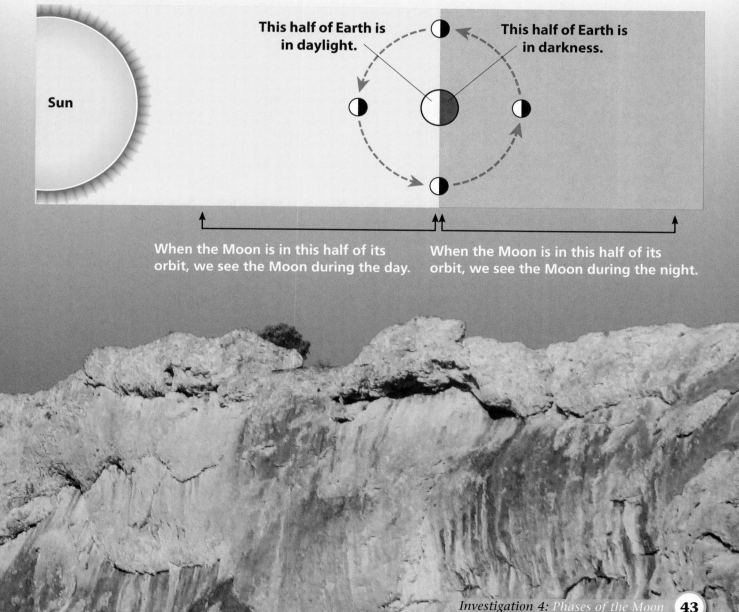

Sun

This half of Earth is in daylight.

This half of Earth is in darkness.

When the Moon is in this half of its orbit, we see the Moon during the day.

When the Moon is in this half of its orbit, we see the Moon during the night.

Day and Night

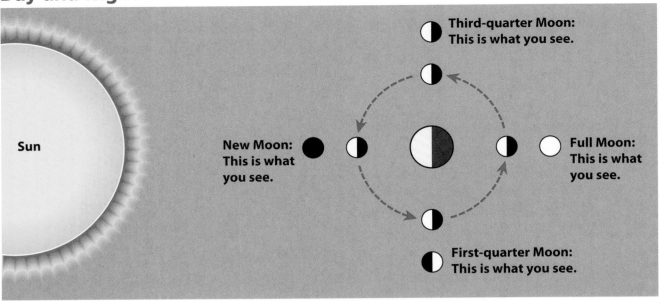

Sun

New Moon:
This is what you see.

Third-quarter Moon:
This is what you see.

Full Moon:
This is what you see.

First-quarter Moon:
This is what you see.

Our view of the Moon changes during its orbit as we see more or less of its sunlit side. This is why the Moon appears to change shape day by day.

The Lunar Cycle

The Moon changes through its phases in a predictable pattern. At the new Moon, the Moon is aligned with the Sun. The first appearance of the Moon after the new Moon is a thin crescent. The Moon is very closely aligned with the Sun. The next day the crescent will be a little bigger as it moved farther and farther from alignment with the Sun. The Moon has moved in its orbit, so that we can see a little bit more of the lit part, and a little bit less of the dark part. The crescent will get bigger each day until the first-quarter Moon. Getting bigger is called **waxing**.

After the first quarter, the Moon continues waxing. But it is no longer a crescent Moon. It is a **gibbous** Moon. The gibbous Moon has a shape that is smaller than a full Moon, but more than a quarter Moon. The gibbous Moon waxes until it appears completely round. That is the full Moon.

On your Moon log, you drew the shape of the Moon for a month. If you repeated the process over and over, that pattern is what you would see each cycle. That is the lunar cycle that you will observe month after month.

Phases of the Moon

| New Moon | Waxing crescent | First quarter | Waxing gibbous | Full Moon | Waning gibbous | Third quarter | Waning crescent |

The Moon passes through a cycle of eight phases during one revolution around Earth.

During a total solar eclipse, only the Sun's glowing outer atmosphere, or corona, can be seen. But never look at it directly!

For the next 2 weeks, the Moon is **waning**. Each day it appears to be a little smaller. The Moon has moved in its orbit, so that we can see a little bit more of the dark part and a little bit less of the light part. The waning gibbous Moon becomes the third-quarter Moon. Then the Moon becomes a waning crescent Moon as it moves closer to alignment with the Sun. At the end of just over 4 weeks, the lunar cycle is complete. The Moon is new again.

Eclipses

Occasionally, people on Earth observe a lovely orange-colored eclipse of the Moon (a **lunar eclipse**). Less frequently, we observe a black-centered eclipse of the Sun (a **solar eclipse**).

What causes these interesting events? During which Moon phase can you see a lunar eclipse? During which Moon phase can you see a solar eclipse?

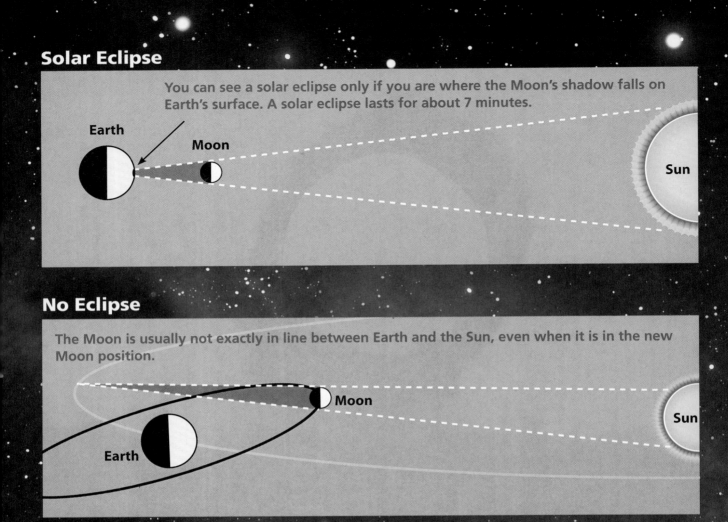

Solar Eclipse

You can see a solar eclipse only if you are where the Moon's shadow falls on Earth's surface. A solar eclipse lasts for about 7 minutes.

Earth

Moon

Sun

No Eclipse

The Moon is usually not exactly in line between Earth and the Sun, even when it is in the new Moon position.

Moon

Sun

Earth

Solar eclipse. A total solar eclipse occurs when the Moon passes exactly between Earth and the Sun. The Moon completely hides the disk of the Sun when this happens.

The place where a solar eclipse can be observed is restricted to a very small location on Earth's surface. A total eclipse of the Sun can be observed for several minutes as the disk of the Moon passes across the disk of the Sun.

The Moon travels around Earth in about 1 month. Why doesn't a solar eclipse occur every month? The Moon's orbit around Earth is not in the same plane as the orbit of Earth around the Sun. The Moon's orbit is tilted a little bit, so most months the Moon, the Sun, and Earth do not align exactly.

Lunar Eclipse

You can see a lunar eclipse if you are on the night side of Earth when the Moon is in Earth's shadow. A total lunar eclipse can last as long as 1 hour and 40 minutes.

No Eclipse

Earth's shadow does not fall on the Moon in most months, so no lunar eclipse is observed, even when the Moon is in the full Moon position.

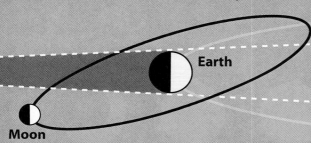

Lunar eclipse. An eclipse of the Moon occurs when Earth passes exactly between the Moon and the Sun. The Moon moves into Earth's shadow during a lunar eclipse. At the time of a full lunar eclipse, Earth's shadow completely covers the disk of the Moon.

Why don't we see a lunar eclipse every month? Because of the tilt of the Moon's orbit around Earth, Earth's shadow does not fall on the Moon in most months. And to make things even more complicated, the orientation of the Moon's orbital plane changes a little bit each year.

During a total lunar eclipse, the Moon is darkened or reddened as it is entirely in Earth's shadow.

Lunar Eclipse Sequence

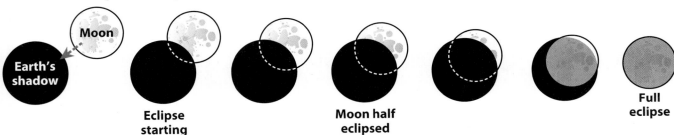

This occurs as the Moon moves in its counterclockwise orbit around Earth, passes into Earth's shadow, and ends up completely eclipsed. The reddish-brown color of the last image is typical of a fully eclipsed Moon.

Why is the fully eclipsed Moon reddish-brown and not invisible? When light passes through Earth's atmosphere, it is bent and scattered by the air particles. As a result, instead of ending up in a completely black shadow, some reddish light falls on the Moon's surface, making it appear reddish-brown. If this bending and scattering did not occur, a totally eclipsed Moon would be invisible because no light would hit the Moon and no light would be reflected back into our eyes on Earth.

Think Questions

1. **What would you tell a student who thinks the Moon is only visible at night?**
2. **Why is a lunar eclipse during a full Moon?**
3. **Why is a solar eclipse during a new Moon?**

Craters: Real and Simulated

Looking at the Moon through a telescope, the first things you notice are the craters. Big craters, little craters, huge craters, and even craters that overlap.

Some areas seem devoid of **craters** while others are covered. What created the craters on the Moon? Was it mostly volcanic activity or **impacts**? For years, scientists were not sure. Two geologists debated these questions in the early 1960s. Jack Green (1925–2014) thought the craters were inactive volcanoes. Gene Shoemaker (1928–1997) thought the craters were scars from impacts on the Moon's surface.

Both geologists looked for evidence to support their claims. One piece of the evidence that helped answer the question was shocked quartz. This mineral turned up in underground test sites for nuclear bombs. Shocked quartz forms under tremendous pressure, like that generated by a nuclear explosion. Shoemaker found shocked quartz inside the Barringer Crater in Arizona. The shocked quartz confirmed that this crater resulted from an impact. A volcano would not generate enough pressure to create shocked quartz.

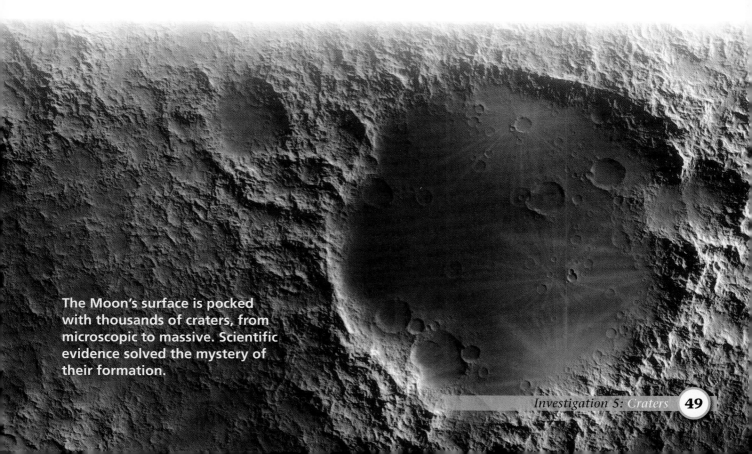

The Moon's surface is pocked with thousands of craters, from microscopic to massive. Scientific evidence solved the mystery of their formation.

Green and Shoemaker agreed that if they could examine Moon rocks from the larger craters, they would have enough evidence to know which process produced the craters on the Moon. The Apollo missions provided the rock samples that confirmed the impact theory.

Collisions

The solar system was young over 4 billion years ago. A huge number of small objects were flying around and colliding. Sometimes, the objects broke into smaller pieces. Other times, they stuck together. In the first half billion years of the solar system, violent collisions were very frequent. There was no chance of life on any planet with all these collisions.

Even today, countless small- and medium-sized pieces of rock and metal, called **meteoroids**, orbit the Sun. Tiny particles rain down on Earth every day. Most of them slow down and burn up in Earth's atmosphere. Slightly larger ones, gravel- and pebble-sized, streak across the night sky. These **meteors** are also known as shooting stars.

The Moon's lack of atmosphere means there's no erosion to change or erase the cratery moonscape.

This artist's depiction of an asteroid about to strike Earth looks like science fiction. But is it?

But the atmosphere only slows and burns small objects. Larger objects move right through the atmosphere as easily as a stone through a spider web. Some of these are relatively small, and some are the size of cities. These larger objects are called **asteroids**. Many asteroids are orbiting the Sun between the orbits of Mars and Jupiter. This region is the **asteroid belt**. Many other asteroids have orbits that go through the inner solar system. When a meteoroid or an asteroid hits a moon or a planet, it creates a crater. Tiny meteors make craters that are microscopic. Large asteroids can produce huge craters. You could walk many hours or even days to cross one of these craters.

Icy objects, called **comets**, sometimes fly through the inner solar system. Comets orbit the Sun. Most of the time, they are beyond the outermost planets in the solar system, in the **Oort Cloud**.

A comet can take decades or even hundreds of years to complete one orbit. A comet might end up on a collision course with a moon or a planet. Comet Shoemaker-Levy 9 neared Jupiter in 1994. Jupiter's **gravity** ripped it into more than 20 pieces, which hit the planet. If a comet or an asteroid of this magnitude were to hit the Moon, the resulting crater would be a major feature on the Moon's surface.

Simulations

Scientists and students can simulate impacts to study crater formation. Sand or flour simulates the Moon's surface. Marbles or rocks simulate meteoroids. The "meteoroids" drop on the surface material. The resulting craters have the characteristic hole, rim, **ejecta**, and **rays** of natural craters. But one thing is different. The speed of the marble or rock is far slower than the speed of debris traveling through space. It is impossible for a marble to represent what really happens when a meteoroid or an asteroid slams into the Moon.

A meteoroid traveling 72,000 kilometers (km) per hour (20 km per second) crashing into the Moon will cause major damage. The impact releases a tremendous amount of energy. The force of the impact creates so much pressure and thermal energy that the meteoroid can explode and disappear. The explosion creates the crater by blasting the soil away.

Scientists have studied crater formation on Earth. They observe the results of explosions at bomb test sites in large expanses of sand. These events are similar to what happens when a meteoroid hits.

Take Note

Review the procedure and findings of the crater experiment from class. Make a new notebook entry. Explain how your experiment was similar to and different from an actual meteoroid impact.

Crater Formation Simulation

Dropping marbles into flour is one way you can simulate crater formation on the Moon's surface.

Simple craters are circular, bowl-shaped depressions.

Terraced craters have stepped walls caused by landslides.

This typical complex crater has a central peak.

Can you see the circular shape of the original impact crater? Can you see craters that have since formed on the dark surface of the mare?

Simple and Complex Craters

Small explosions produce small bowl-shaped craters with a fairly even blanket of ejecta around the rim. These are called **simple craters**.

Larger explosions produce a lot of pressure below the impact. The shock wave after the explosion often pushes up a big mountain in the middle of the crater. **Complex craters** often have central peaks, and ejecta thrown out in long rays.

Really big complex craters also have terraces. They look like giant steps leading from the crater floor up to the rim.

In the past, the Moon had a molten core. Sometimes, an impact was so huge that it cracked the outer layers of the Moon. Magma would seep up and create a **flooded crater**. When the magma cooled, the dark rock became smooth and uniform. This rock creates a **mare** (plural **maria**). Later impacts can make new marks in the mare.

Take Note

Describe the shape of the original impact crater. Can you see craters that have formed on the dark surface of the mare? What is older, the mare or the craters?

Comparing Models to Actual Craters

In class, you simulated the formation of craters on the Moon by dropping marbles into flour. You produced craters like those seen on the Moon. How are these craters like real Moon craters, and how are they different?

Size of craters. Your craters are 2–3 centimeters (cm) in **diameter**. The smallest Moon craters are microscopic. The largest one, the Aitken basin at the Moon's south pole, is 2,500 km across and 13 km deep. It would cover most of the United States! The Imbrium basin (Mare Imbrium), another large impact crater, is 1,200 km across.

Size of projectiles. Your marbles are approximately 1.5 cm in diameter. Scientists believe the asteroid that created the Imbrium basin was 100 km in diameter. A meteoroid as large as New Hampshire can create a crater almost as large as the continental United States. The objects that made the craters on the Moon varied in size.

This impact crater was formed 50,000 years ago when a meteorite struck Earth in the Arizona desert. Scientists believe that the nickel-iron meteorite, 45 m wide and weighing 300,000 tons, vaporized on impact.

Speed of projectiles. Dropped from a height of 200 cm, or 2 meters (m), your marbles reach a speed of perhaps 1 km per hour. The asteroids and meteoroids that struck the Moon were traveling at speeds of about 72,000 km per hour! Unlike Earth, the Moon has no atmosphere to slow a meteoroid as it approaches the surface.

Impact. When your marbles strike the flour, a splash of flour sprays out across the surface of the pan. On the Moon, large meteoroids hit and exploded. The thermal energy generated by the impact is so intense that the rock and the meteoroid instantly vaporize. Expanding gases cause an explosion. It blasts a huge hole and throws debris in all directions. So a 100 km object can create a crater with a diameter of 1,200 km.

Take Note

Draw a line of learning under your notebook entry that compares the crater experiment to an actual impact. Add ideas using information from this article.

Think Questions

The photo below is Barringer Crater in Arizona. Think about how it might have formed.

1. Is it a simple or complex crater?
2. How old do you think it might be? Why?
3. Why do you think Earth has so few craters and the Moon has so many?

Scientists now believe that the mass extinction that occurred around 65 million years ago had its origins in outer space.

The Disappearance of the Dinosaurs

The Earth is about 4.6 billion years old. Changes in populations of plants and animals usually are slow, over millions of years. However, 65 million years ago, populations changed in a geologic instant.

Mass Extinction

Sometimes many species die at about the same time. These events are called mass extinctions. The last mass extinction was 65 million years ago, when the dinosaurs became extinct. About 50 percent to 75 percent of all other species also died out. The age of reptiles ended, and the age of mammals began.

Behind Dr. Walter Alvarez and his wife is the geological clue that unlocked a mystery: a thin layer of iridium-rich clay that coincides with the end of the Age of Dinosaurs.

Climate change probably caused this mass extinction. Two theories about the cause of the climate change are active volcanism and a huge asteroid or comet impact. One or both of these happened about 65 million years ago. The climate change event separated the Cretaceous and Tertiary periods. Most species did not survive the event. It took many thousands of years for new life-forms to repopulate Earth.

Dinosaurs ruled Earth for 165 million years. Their fossils are found in sedimentary rocks that formed when layers of sand, dust, clay, and ash piled up. Over time, they turned into rock. Deep layers of rock are older than the layers above. Older fossils are found in the deeper layers of rock. The fossil record shows that about 65 million years ago, all living dinosaurs vanished.

Looking for Evidence

In the 1970s, Walter Alvarez (1940–), a geologist, was investigating sedimentary rocks on a mountain in Italy. He found an unusual amount of iridium. The element iridium is rare on Earth's surface. But some meteoroids and asteroids are rich in iridium.

Alvarez tested the thin layer of rock that held iridium. It was 65 million years old. Alvarez reasoned that a big asteroid impact might account for the iridium in his rock samples.

Dust and debris from a large impact would have been widely scattered. Alvarez and his research group wondered if an iridium layer would be found in 65-million-year-old sedimentary rocks from other places on Earth. Dust and debris from a large impact would likely be scattered far and wide. When the researchers looked, they found high concentrations of iridium in rocks of the same age in many other places on Earth.

The research group described a likely process. One big impact could have blasted a huge amount of dust, including iridium, into the atmosphere. Global winds carried the dust for months. Gradually, it settled out of the atmosphere all over Earth.

The Dinosaur Connection

Alvarez and his group knew that the extinction of the dinosaurs and the possible asteroid impact happened at about the same time. Could one asteroid impact have caused the extinction of dinosaurs all over Earth?

Even far from the impact site, the giant asteroid collision caused debris to rain down and the atmosphere to become toxic. Along with the dinosaurs, about three quarters of the planet's species disappeared.

The immediate effect of the cataclysmic asteroid strike was intense heat and a massive firestorm. Then, debris and soot blocked the Sun, causing months of darkness and cold.

A big impact on Earth would have dramatic effects. Imagine an asteroid 10 kilometers (km) in diameter. It vaporizes as it blasts a crater 160 km wide and 8 km deep. The blast sends a huge amount of material into the atmosphere and into space. Shock waves from the blast create tsunamis several kilometers high. As the waves travel hundreds of kilometers, they flood and crush everything in their paths.

The blast also creates wind speeds of hundreds of kilometers per hour. Storms rage for weeks. Intense heat from the blast and from hot ash raining on Earth start forest fires. The fires spread out over Earth, destroying nearly half its forests. The intense heat and pressure cause chemical reactions and create acid rain. The resulting acidic waters kill many aquatic organisms.

A huge cloud of very fine material rises from the impact site. It combines with the dust and smoke from forest fires to block out sunlight. Alvarez and other scientists used **models** to estimate the length of the blackout. The asteroid could throw enough material into the atmosphere to block the Sun for a year. Temperatures drop to freezing. Most plants die. Most animals that survived the impact die because they have nothing to eat. Only a few tough organisms in a few protected areas survive.

The Search for More Evidence

This theory had a problem. The impact should have left a very large crater, at least 160 km in diameter. Years of searching uncovered no evidence of such a crater. Perhaps the impact site was hidden under the ocean, which covers about two-thirds of Earth's surface.

Since geologists started to search for the impact crater that killed the dinosaurs, new technologies have emerged. Advanced magnetic sensors help scientists find ancient features of the land. Satellite sensors can "see" through water. An interesting structure showed up in the Gulf of Mexico.

Chicxulub Crater

The impact structure is Chicxulub (CHICK•shoe•lube) Crater. Its center is near the town of Chicxulub, in Yucatán. The crater is one of the largest impact structures in the world. It is more than 180 km in diameter. That is even larger than the crater predicted by the Alvarez team.

Glen Penfield, a geophysicist, discovered the crater in 1978. Rock samples from the site contain shocked quartz, good evidence for the impact origin of the crater. Further investigation of the crater site revealed tektites, glassy pieces usually found in meteor impacts, and other evidence that suggested a huge impact.

This shaded-relief image shows the north side of Mexico's Yucatán peninsula. Color indicates elevation. The green land is at low elevations, rising through yellow and tan to gray at the highest elevations. The dotted line shows the crater rim. It is below rocks that formed long after the impact.

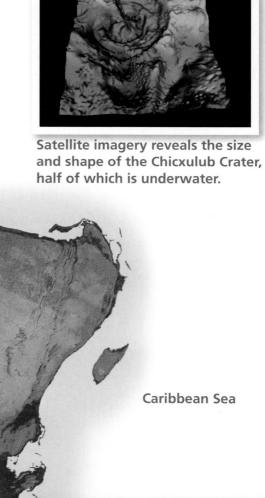

Satellite imagery reveals the size and shape of the Chicxulub Crater, half of which is underwater.

Outer rim of Chicxulub Crater

Gulf of Mexico

Yucatán peninsula of Mexico

Caribbean Sea

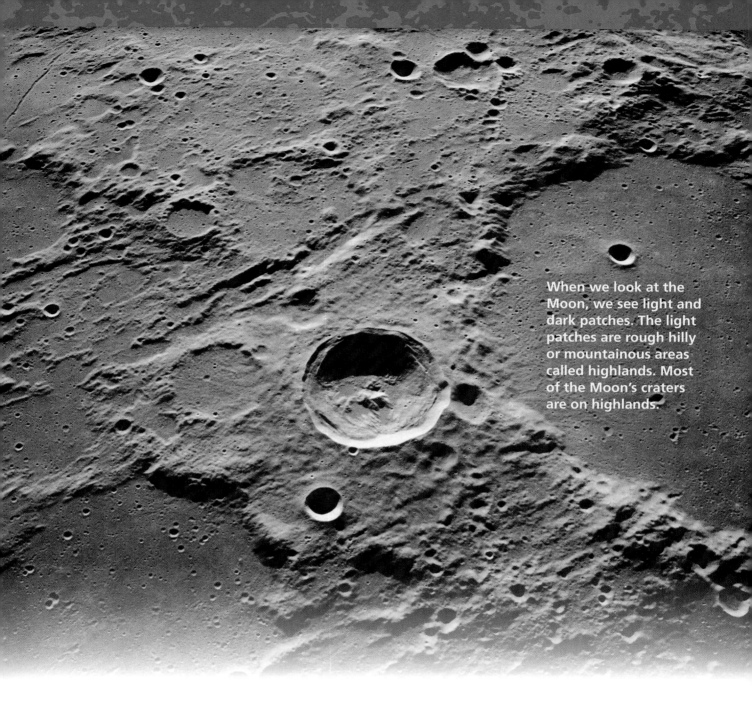

When we look at the Moon, we see light and dark patches. The light patches are rough hilly or mountainous areas called highlands. Most of the Moon's craters are on highlands.

Future Earth Impacts

Earth and the Moon share a similar history in the solar system. Both formed about 4.6 billion years ago. And both have been hit by asteroids and comets. Craters on Earth do not last very long in geologic time. Wind and moving water erases them. Craters on the Moon are not erased by wind or water because the Moon has no air or liquid water.

The Moon can be used as a "cosmic scorecard" for impacts. The oldest parts of the Moon are the light **highlands** areas. They have too many craters to count, because collisions happened so often in the early solar system. The impact rate was over a thousand times what it is today. The dark maria, though younger, are a better scorecard.

Dark, smooth maria formed about 4 billion years ago, providing a convenient timeline for those figuring out the Moon's history. Craters found on maria must have formed sometime in the last 4 billion years.

Moon rocks show that the dark maria formed less than 4 billion years ago. At first, these smooth flows of molten rock were craterless. Every crater we see today on these maria represents an impact during the last 4 billion years. We can count the big craters in the maria, divide by 4 billion years, and get an idea of how frequently objects hit the maria. Earth gets hit by a big object at about the same rate. And Earth's cross section is about 64 times larger than the surface area of the maria, so we need to factor that in.

Did You Know?

Count how many craters there are in the maria regions of the Moon. Multiply that by 64, and divide by 4 billion years. The result is an estimate of how often Earth gets hit by a large object, on average.

Think Questions

1. What kinds of animals might have survived the period of reduced light after the asteroid impact?
2. If a huge impact created a new crater like Chicxulub today, what might be the result worldwide?
3. How often does such a big object hit Earth?

Gene Shoemaker: Planetary Geologist

Eugene "Gene" Merle Shoemaker (1928–1997) was a planetary scientist. He specialized in meteor impacts and their effects on the solar system. He dreamed of going to the Moon, a great place to study craters.

Early Work

Shoemaker was born in Los Angeles, California. He graduated from the California Institute of Technology in Pasadena at the age of 19. He got a master's degree in geology only a year later. He joined the US Geological Survey in 1948. It sent him to explore for uranium deposits in Colorado and Utah. This work brought him near an impact site named Barringer Crater, near Winslow, Arizona.

Desert areas are convenient for mining because, with little vegetation and few bodies of water, the bedrock tends to be exposed. These same characteristics made it possible for Shoemaker to thoroughly study an impact crater on Earth.

From 1957 to 1960, Shoemaker carried out pioneering work on the nature and origin of Barringer Crater. Shoemaker and his colleague Edward C. T. Chao (1919–2008) discovered coesite in the rubble at the bottom of Barringer Crater. Coesite is a form of shocked quartz, a mineral created only during impacts. Shoemaker also found coesite in the Ries basin in Germany. It confirmed that the basin is a giant impact structure.

Coesite became a tool to identify many more impact structures on Earth. The discovery of coesite eventually led to the theory that huge impacts might have caused mass extinctions.

Planetary Geology

A man of vision, Shoemaker wanted to extend geologic studies into space. He helped train the Apollo astronauts. He talked about the Moon's geology during newscasts of the Moon walks.

During the 1960s, Shoemaker led teams that investigated the structure and history of the Moon. They mapped the Moon's geology, using telescope images. Eventually, their methods were used on other solar-system Apollo programs. His Moon studies continued in 1994, when he was science team leader for the Clementine project.

Young Gene Shoemaker's modeling of a rocket belt is a glimpse into his desire to be the first geologist-astronaut.

Shoemaker's claim to fame was his research on the formation of impact craters. He studied them on the Moon, Earth, and other planetary bodies. He also discovered many asteroids and comets that cross Earth's orbital path. Shoemaker, his wife Carolyn (1929–), and a colleague, David Levy (1948–), discovered Comet Shoemaker-Levy 9. Pieces of this comet crashed into Jupiter in July 1994 as astronomers watched from afar. It was the first time an extraterrestrial impact was directly observed. Together, the Shoemakers were the leading discoverers of comets in the 20th century. They also discovered more than 800 asteroids.

Honors

The University of Arizona awarded Shoemaker an honorary doctorate of science in 1984. In 1992, President George H. W. Bush gave Shoemaker the National Medal of Science, the highest science honor given in the United States.

From the time he was a teenager, Shoemaker wanted to go to the Moon. In his early career, he dreamed of being the first geologist to map the Moon. However, a health problem prevented Shoemaker from becoming an astronaut. Shortly before Shoemaker died, he said, "Not going to the Moon and banging on it with my own hammer has been the biggest disappointment in life."

Shoemaker died in a car accident. At the time, he was searching for meteor craters in Australia. Wherever he went, he shared his enthusiasm for geology and love of the land.

Shoemaker's research at the Barringer Crater proved that the structure was an impact crater. He extended these studies into space, applying geologic principles to planetary mapping.

After he died, Shoemaker's dream came true. His colleagues and friends put a small capsule in the Lunar Prospector spacecraft. The capsule held some of Shoemaker's remains. The capsule rode in a vacuum-sealed aluminum sleeve inside the spacecraft. It was wrapped in brass foil. The foil was inscribed with images of Comet Hale-Bopp and Barringer Crater and a quotation from Shakespeare's *Romeo and Juliet*.

The tiny Lunar Prospector successfully crash-landed in a dark crater on the Moon on August 31, 1999. It deposited the ashes of Gene Shoemaker on the lunar surface. It was a fine tribute to the great planetary geologist who said his biggest dream was to go to the Moon.

Think Questions

1. **What evidence did Shoemaker find to support that Barringer Crater was the result of an impact?**
2. **How did Shoemaker learn about the Moon's geology without going there?**

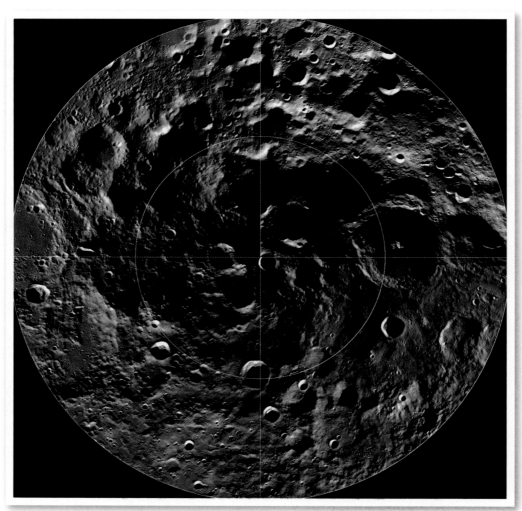

The south pole of the Moon, shown here, is where the Lunar Prospector impacted at the end of its extensive Moon study. The low solar angle creates long shadows at the poles, making this area appear extra dark.

The Cosmos in a Nutshell

The universe is big. How big? So big that we need to use special units.

Here on Earth, we measure distance in meters and kilometers. These units are way too short for measuring distance in the solar system and the cosmos. We measure those huge distances in **astronomical units** (AU) and **light-years** (ly).

Measuring Distance

One astronomical unit is the average distance between Earth and the Sun, about 150 million kilometers (km). One ly is the distance light travels in 1 year, at the speed of about 300,000 km per second. One light-year is equal to about 9.5 trillion km, which is equal to about 63,000 AU. The closest star to us, other than the Sun, is about 4 ly away.

So if we are recording a distance in astronomical units, it is a relatively small distance, compared to a light-year.

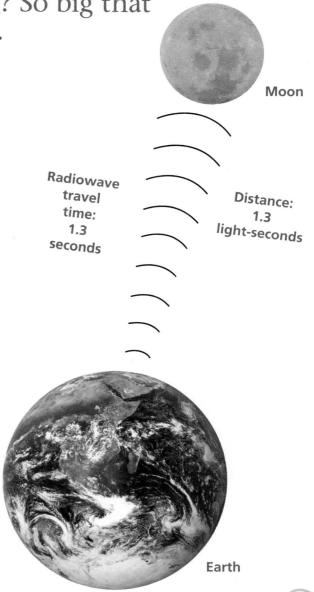

Moon

Radiowave travel time: 1.3 seconds

Distance: 1.3 light-seconds

Earth

We can use the terms *light-second*, *light-minute*, and *light-hour* as subunits for measuring distance.

One light-second is the distance light travels in a second. Radio waves also travel at the speed of light. To talk to an astronaut on the Moon, we use radio waves. A radio signal takes about 1.3 seconds to go from Earth to the Moon, so the Moon is about 1.3 light-seconds away.

One light-minute is the distance light travels in a minute. It takes about 8.5 light-minutes, the time it takes to eat an apple, for light to reach us from the Sun. We can say the Sun is a little more than 8 light-minutes away. To send radio signals to spacecraft on or near Mars can take as little as 5 minutes or as long as 20 minutes. The distance between Earth and Mars varies from about 5 to 20 light-minutes, depending on where the two planets are in their orbits.

One light-hour is the distance light travels in an hour. Sending radio waves to spacecraft visiting the outer planets of the solar system takes hours. It takes at least 1 hour and 20 minutes for radio waves to get to Saturn, and sometimes more than 4 hours to get to Neptune.

Among stars, the Sun is of medium size and average brightness. But in our solar system, there's nothing average about it! It contains most of the mass and provides most of the energy.

The Solar System

The solar system is a region of space that includes the Sun and all things orbiting it. In rough order of size, from largest to smallest, those orbiting objects are the major planets, their **satellites** (moons), asteroids, comets, meteoroids, and dust. The Sun accounts for about 99.8 percent of the mass of the solar system. The 0.2 percent that did not fall into the Sun forms everything else in the solar system.

Planets. A planet is massive enough for its own gravity to shape it into a sphere. Planets orbit a star. The number of known planets in the solar system has changed over the years. In ancient times, Earth's status as a planet was not understood. Only the five brightest planets (Mercury, Venus, Mars, Jupiter, and Saturn) were known. But few, if any, people thought these planets orbited the Sun. When telescopes were invented, other planets were discovered. Uranus was discovered in 1781 and Neptune in 1846.

In 1930, Pluto was discovered and added to the list of planets, bringing the count to nine. But over time, more Pluto-like objects were discovered in the outer reaches of the solar system. Members of the International Astronomical Union (IAU) had to decide what to call the new objects. Should they all be called planets?

The debate was quite intense. Some members defined *planet* based mostly on a minimum size. Others wanted to include the planet's gravity. It had to be able to draw in small local objects. **Dwarf planet** was the new category of solar system objects created that included Pluto and similar objects. A dwarf planet orbits the Sun, is big enough to be round, but does not pull in the objects near it. The current solar system count now stands at eight planets and five dwarf planets.

Other solar-system objects. A satellite is an object orbiting a larger object. Natural objects orbiting a planet are moons. (We usually distinguish Earth's Moon from other moons by capitalizing the word.) Probes launched into orbit around Earth or other planets are called artificial satellites.

Pluto, with its moon Charon in the background, was once classified as a planet. New discoveries led astronomers to create a new category for Pluto and other small planet-like objects: dwarf planet. (Pluto and Charon are shown to scale for size, but are not to scale for distance.)

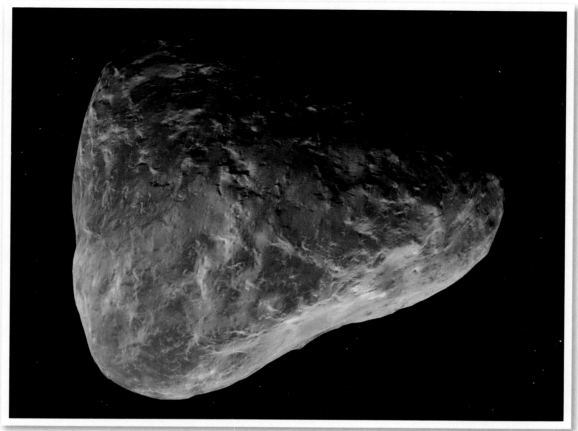

Millions of irregular-shaped rocky objects called asteroids revolve around the Sun, mainly in the asteroid belt between Mars and Jupiter. Most are less than 1 km in diameter, but some are much larger.

An asteroid is a small, rocky object that orbits the Sun. Most asteroids orbit between the orbits of Mars and Jupiter. But many asteroids have orbits that take them closer to the Sun than Earth's orbit does. Others have orbits that take them well beyond Jupiter. The largest asteroid between Jupiter and Mars is named Ceres. It is about as wide as the state of Texas. Ceres is large enough to be called a dwarf planet.

A meteoroid is a bit of solid debris in space. Small meteoroids (dust-sized to pebble-sized) enter Earth's atmosphere at an average speed of about 40,000 km per hour. They vaporize due to friction with the air. They leave a streak of light across the night sky, which is called a meteor. Meteors are also called shooting stars, although they are nothing like stars. If a meteoroid survives the friction of the atmosphere, the pieces that hit the ground are called **meteorites**.

Did You Know?

Meteoroid: a bit of solid debris in space
Meteor: a streak of light in the night sky, caused by a meteoroid vaporizing after entering Earth's atmosphere. A meteor is also called a shooting star.
Meteorite: a meteoroid that has hit the ground

This image of Comet Tempel 1 was taken 67 seconds after the *Deep Impact* spacecraft deliberately smashed into it to find out more about comets.

Beyond the orbit of Neptune is a region of the solar system called the **Kuiper Belt**. The Kuiper Belt contains millions of small objects. While the asteroids between Mars and Jupiter are mostly made of rock and metal, Kuiper Belt objects are ice. The ice includes water and methane or ammonia. More than 1,000 Kuiper Belt objects have been discovered. The Kuiper Belt extends from about 30 AU from the Sun out to about 55 AU.

A comet is a chunk of ice, dust, and rock a few kilometers in size. When a comet comes close to the Sun, the Sun's energy heats the surface until it **emits** gas and dust. Comets can develop one or two tails made of gas and dust.

A comet's tail always points away from the Sun, no matter what direction the comet is moving. That's because solar wind disperses the material boiled off the comet's surface.

The Seagull Nebula, a complex of gas and dust clouds with many bright young stars, has a bird-like appearance from Earth. The "wingspan" is about 100 ly across.

Comets spend most of their time very far from the Sun. They have very long, oval orbits. Their tails are visible for only a few weeks or months as they swing quickly around the Sun. Beyond the Kuiper Belt, astronomers think there might be a huge sphere of icy matter. This region, called the Oort Cloud, might be the origin of comets. It could be a couple of light-years in diameter.

Take Note

The objects discussed here are all part of the solar system. Review your notebook entry *Looking at the Cosmos*. Make any necessary changes to your solar system list.

Nebulae

A **nebula** (plural **nebulae**) is a cloud of gas and dust in space between stars. *Nebula* is Latin for cloud. Some nebulae glow with their own light. Some nebulae scatter light from stars within them. Some block light from things behind them.

One way to classify nebulae is by how they relate to the evolution and lifespans of stars. Many nebulae have new stars forming. In fact, a single nebula can be so huge that it could be the birthplace for a whole cluster of stars. But a nebula can also be leftover dust and debris after a star dies. When a large star dies, it can leave behind a **supernova** remnant, such as the Crab Nebula.

Stars

The Sun is an average-sized star. Stars are large, hot balls of gas. They generate energy in their cores by nuclear reactions. Most stars are very stable. Depending on size, they can have lifespans ranging from a few hundred thousand years to several billion years. Slow-burning dwarf stars can live even longer. Stars radiate in different colors, depending on how hot they are. Red stars are the coolest (over 2,000 degrees Celsius [°C] on the surface), and blue stars are the hottest (over 10,000°C on the surface). Our closest star, the Sun, is a yellow star (5,500°C).

The image shows Earth's size compared to the Sun (but the distance is not to scale). In 5 billion years or so, Earth could be engulfed by the Sun if it becomes a red giant.

A system of two stars orbiting each other is called a **binary star**. Multiple-star systems have three or more stars. About half of all stars are members of multiple-star systems. Alpha Centauri, the nearest star to the Sun, is a triple-star system with two stars similar to our Sun and one small, red star. They all orbit around one another.

A star's life. Very large, massive stars burn fuel much faster than smaller stars. Their lifespan may be only a few hundred thousand years. Smaller stars will live on for billions of years because the nuclear reactions take place much more slowly. Eventually, the star's fuel will begin to run out.

Many average-sized stars in the final stages of their lives can become **red giants**. A red giant is very large and has a relatively cool surface. If the Sun becomes a red giant, in perhaps 5 billion years, its surface might extend past the orbit of Mars.

An average-sized star can shrink and become a **white dwarf**. This happens after its red-giant phase and after it has no more fuel for nuclear reactions. White dwarfs shine only by radiating away their stored-up thermal energy. A white dwarf as massive as the Sun may shrink to the size of Earth, or 1/100 of its original size. It can become so compressed and dense that a teaspoonful of its material would weigh as much as a truck.

In comparison, a very large star can become a supernova. These huge explosions can generate more light than all the other stars in the galaxy combined. A supernova can shine brightly for several days.

Earth

Black holes. Once a large star becomes a supernova, the remains at the core form a very dense object. This object can be either a neutron star or a **black hole**. For stars that are 1.3 to 2 times as massive as the Sun, pressures in the supernova force the electrons of atoms into the atoms' nuclei. There they combine with protons and create neutrons. The entire mass of this neutron star is crammed into a ball only about 10 km across. A spoonful of material in a neutron star would weigh more than all the automobiles in the United States put together.

For more massive stars, a black hole can form after the star becomes a supernova.

Black holes are so dense that even the neutrons are crushed. The gravitational pull is so strong that nothing can escape from inside the black hole, not even light.

Star Clusters

A **star cluster** is a group of stars held together by gravitational attraction. An open star cluster has a few dozen to several hundred stars. Open star clusters are sometimes found in a nebula, indicating that the stars have just formed.

This illustration shows what it might look like as a star is "captured," torn apart, and consumed by a supermassive black hole. Material from the shredded star generates a huge flare of light.

The spiral Andromeda galaxy is the closest major galaxy to our own. Appearing in the night sky like a smudge of light about the size of the full Moon, it is the most distant object visible with the unaided eye.

A globular star cluster is spherical. It is larger than open star clusters and has older stars. A globular star cluster can contain hundreds of thousands to a few million stars. About 150 globular star clusters form a huge halo around the **Milky Way**.

Galaxies

A galaxy is a collection of tens of millions to hundreds of billions of stars, interstellar gas, and dust. A galaxy is held together by the gravity of its stars, which revolve around the center of the galaxy. There is good evidence that a supermassive black hole is at the center of many large galaxies. These black holes have a mass equal to that of millions of stars.

The most common type of galaxy is the flattened spiral. Elliptical galaxies are oval, with no spiral patterns. A few galaxies are irregular. Our Milky Way galaxy is a spiral galaxy.

The Large Magellanic Cloud is a satellite galaxy to the Milky Way. That is, it's a dwarf galaxy that orbits our galaxy.

The Local Group

From Earth, we see part of the Milky Way as a faint band of hazy light. It stretches all the way across the sky from north to south. It can be seen only from clear, dark locations. Through binoculars or a small telescope, we can see that it is made of vast numbers of faint stars. The Milky Way is the disk of our spiral galaxy, seen from our location near the edge of the disk.

The Milky Way is about 100,000 ly across. It contains roughly 400 billion stars. The Sun is about two-thirds of the way out from the center of the galaxy. The Sun completes one counterclockwise orbit around the center of the Milky Way about every 200 million years. The center of our galaxy is believed to be a black hole.

The galaxies closest to the Milky Way are the **Magellanic Clouds**. These galaxies are about 100,000 ly away and can be seen easily from Earth's Southern Hemisphere.

The Milky Way is a member of a relatively small cluster of about two dozen galaxies called the **Local Group**. Most of the Local Group galaxies are considerably smaller than the Milky Way. The only other large galaxy is the Andromeda galaxy, which is about 2 million ly away. The Local Group is about 3 million ly across. It is part of a supercluster of galaxy clusters called the Virgo Cluster. The center of the Virgo Cluster lies in the direction of the constellation Virgo.

The big bang. *Universe* and *cosmos* are words used to describe all things that can be observed or detected. The **big bang theory** explains how the universe came into being. Many astronomical observations support this theory. Astronomers calculate that the big bang happened about 13.73 billion years ago. There was one explosion that formed clusters of galaxies and sent them moving away from one another.

Did You Know?

Turn to your notebook entry *Looking at the Cosmos*. Make any necessary changes to your lists for what is in the solar system, galaxy, and universe.

Think Questions

1. Why did some planets remain undiscovered until after the telescope was invented?
2. What might happen to the Sun in several billion years?

This is an artist's representation of the Milky Way galaxy and the location of the Sun.

The Moon is Earth's closest neighbor in space and Earth's only natural satellite. We can see its features clearly because it is so near and because it has no atmosphere to obscure them.

How Earth Got and Held onto Its Moon

Look up in the night sky, and on most evenings you will see the Moon, familiar and comforting. But was it always there? How did it get there?

Counting out from the Sun, Earth is the first planet with a natural satellite, or moon. Mercury and Venus, nearer to the Sun, don't have a moon. Mars, the fourth planet out, has two moons. These moons are probably two asteroids that got caught by Mars and ended up in its orbit.

It is believed that Earth did not have a moon at first. It acquired one early in its history as a result of a huge planetary collision. Imagine how this event may have

happened, perhaps 4.5 billion years ago.

Earth was more or less a finished planet, but still hot and molten. Its gravity had pulled in most of the dust and gas in the region. These were the early days of the solar system. If you had been there, you would have noticed a lot of material flying around in unstable orbits. Some of the chunks, called **planetesimals**, were the size of small planets.

How the Moon Formed

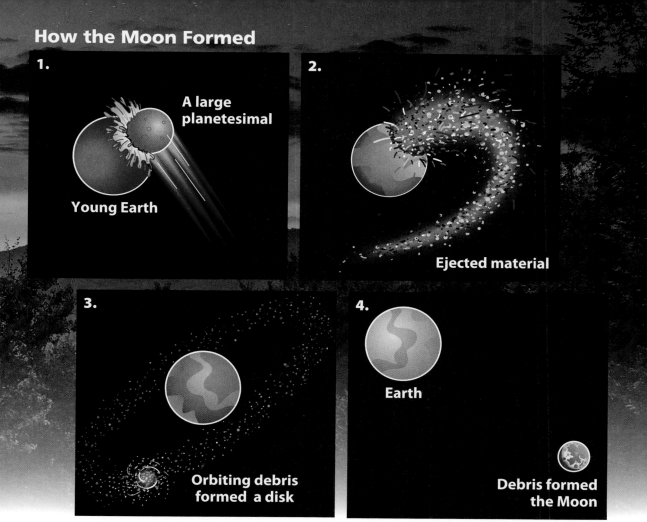

1. A large planetesimal

Young Earth

2. Ejected material

3. Orbiting debris formed a disk

4. Earth

Debris formed the Moon

According to the widely accepted "giant impact" theory, the Moon formed early in Earth's history. A cosmic collision ejected debris into orbit around our young planet.

A Collision Course

Planetary scientists now think that a planetesimal, perhaps the size of Mars, was traveling around the Sun in an orbit that was far from circular. Why did it have such an irregular orbit? Perhaps it was pulled by the gravity of a large planet, or perhaps objects following irregular paths were common in the early solar system. Anyway, it ended up heading for Earth.

Had you been on Earth, here is what you might have observed. The planetesimal first was just a dot in the sky. Over a period of days and weeks, it grew bigger and bigger. At last, it completely blocked the view in that direction. Then it struck. Because the colliding objects were so large, the impact itself seemed to happen in slow motion. It lasted several minutes, even though the planetesimal was traveling at perhaps 40,000 kilometers (km) per hour.

The Explosion

The crash caused a chain of events. First, the impact destroyed the incoming object. The planetesimal was reduced to vapor, dust, and debris. Some pieces plunged into the interior of Earth. A significant portion of Earth disintegrated. The energy that resulted from the crash produced an explosion of unimaginable magnitude. Earth itself might have been in danger of being blasted apart.

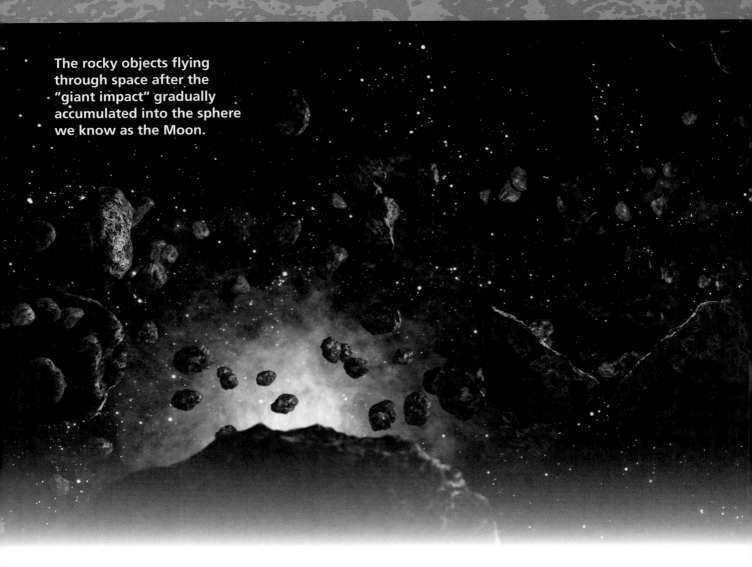

The rocky objects flying through space after the "giant impact" gradually accumulated into the sphere we know as the Moon.

Second, the explosive release of energy threw a tremendous amount of matter into motion—at least 20 billion cubic km. Pieces of matter with great kinetic energy flew into space and were never seen again. Other matter flew up into the air and returned to Earth. Some returned almost immediately as huge rocks. Granules of various sizes returned a little later. The atmosphere held on to dust and chemicals for months or even years.

A lot of the debris did not fly off into space. Nor did it return to Earth. It began orbiting Earth and formed a disk of debris, like the rings of Saturn. The ring was probably about two Earth diameters from the surface of Earth. Over 1 or 2 years, the pieces of matter and dust started to attract one another. Gradually, they formed larger and larger chunks of debris, and eventually formed the Moon.

Earth had a moon where previously there was none. It must have been quite a sight when it was only about 30,000 km above Earth, rather than the 384,000 km of today.

Take Note

How is the Moon's formation like solar-system formation? Explain your ideas in your notebook.

The Role of Gravity

Gravity is one of the four known forces in the universe, along with electromagnetic force and two kinds of nuclear force. These four forces make everything in the world behave in regular ways. The law of universal gravitation tells us that gravity is the force that causes two masses to attract each other. The gravity exerted between two small masses, like a marble and an apple, is so small that we cannot detect it. But the gravity exerted by a large mass, like a planet or a star, is tremendous. The larger the mass, the stronger the force it exerts.

The force of gravity between the Sun and Earth is so strong that it keeps Earth in a circular orbit around the Sun. The circular diagram shows those forces in action. And it shows what would happen to Earth's path without the gravitational attraction.

When the planetesimal hit Earth, some matter was thrown straight up in the air. Two things could have happened to that matter. Chunks of debris thrown with enough speed escaped Earth's gravity and became loose space debris. Debris without enough speed was pulled down to the surface by Earth's gravity.

However, most of the matter ejected by the impact would not go straight up, but would be launched at an angle. Something different could have happened to this matter.

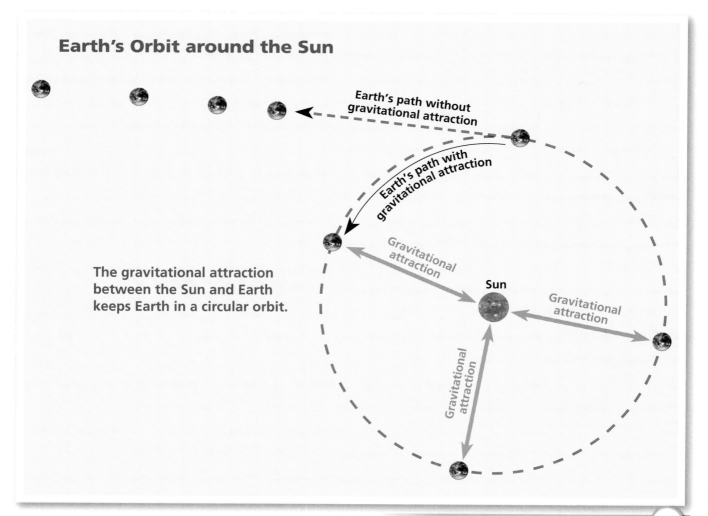

Earth's Orbit around the Sun

Earth's path without gravitational attraction

Earth's path with gravitational attraction

Gravitational attraction

Sun

Gravitational attraction

Gravitational attraction

The gravitational attraction between the Sun and Earth keeps Earth in a circular orbit.

Matter in Motion

Before we get into where that matter went, consider another piece of information about the behavior of matter. Sir Isaac Newton (1643–1727) figured out that an object in motion will travel in a straight line. It changes direction only when a force acts on it. In other words, things do not travel in curves, circles, spirals, or zigzags unless a force (a push or a pull) acts on them to change their motion.

So where did the impact debris go? Most of the matter flew out from the impact at an angle, not straight up. Earth's gravity also acted on this debris. Consider a rock the size of a microwave oven as an example. It flies off in a straight line, but at an angle. If there were no gravity, the rock would just keep going.

Instead, gravity pulls on the rock. Because the rock is going sideways fast, the pull only changes the direction of the rock as it moves. The force of gravity keeps acting on the rock, but it never pulls it all the way down to Earth. The rock travels around and around Earth. This is the definition of an orbit. When the planetesimal hit Earth, a lot of the material was thrown out at an angle just far enough to go into orbit around Earth. Earth's gravity caused it to orbit, and the debris became the Moon.

Did You Know?

Tides are the daily rising and falling of the sea level. The sea level rises and falls in predictable patterns because of the gravitational interaction between the ocean and the Moon as it orbits Earth.

FOSS Visit **FOSSweb** to view the "Tides" online activity and learn more about tides.

The regular rise and fall of the ocean, or tides, are caused by gravity. The force of gravity is an interaction between two masses, in this case the Moon and Earth.

Imagine taking a yo-yo by the end of its string and swinging it around over your head. You have it going in a nice circle. If you let go of the string, what happens? It stops going in a circle and flies off in a straight line. As long as you keep applying a force (pulling on the string) to change the direction of the yo-yo, it continues to orbit your hand.

Gravity is the "string" pulling on the Moon to keep it in a circular path. Similarly, gravity is the force keeping Earth (and the other planets) in a circular orbit around the Sun. In fact, everything that is behaving in a predictable way in the solar system is orbiting something else. And in every case, gravity rules the action.

Take Note

Return to your notebook entry comparing formation of the Moon and of the solar system. Add some ideas about gravity. How did gravity affect each formation?

Think Questions

1. What type of rocks might you expect to find on the Moon? Why do you think that?
2. How can an object enter Earth's orbit?

The Sun and planets in this image are shown to scale for size, but not for distance. As you learned in class, the distances between solar system objects are so great that they are hard to show in a diagram.

A Tour of the Solar System

Imagine that you are coming to the solar system as an alien stranger. A tour guide provides information as you gaze out the window. What will you see?

As you approach, you get a **bird's-eye view** from space. From here, you see the whole solar system. The most surprising thing is that the solar system is mostly empty. The matter is concentrated in tiny dots that are extremely far apart. Most of the dots are planets. In the same way that the Moon is held in orbit around Earth, the planets are held in orbit around the Sun by gravity.

About 109 Earths would fit across the Sun's diameter.

Earth

There is a star in the center of the solar system. Four small planets orbit pretty close to the star. These are the rocky terrestrial planets. Next, there is the asteroid belt, a region of small bits of matter orbiting the star. Out farther, four big gas planets are in orbit around the star. These are the gas giant planets. Beyond the gas giant planets is a huge region of different-sized icy chunks of matter called the Kuiper Belt.

That is all that can be seen from your bird's-eye view in space.

The Sun

The Sun is a star. It is similar in size, color, and brightness to some of the stars you can see in the night sky. The Sun is at the center of the solar system. Everything else in the solar system orbits the Sun. The Sun rules.

The Sun is made mostly of hydrogen (74 percent) and helium (25 percent). It is huge. The diameter is about 1,384,000 kilometers (km). That's about 109 times the diameter of Earth. (See Earth compared to the Sun in the picture.)

The Sun is incredibly hot. Scientists have figured out that the temperature at the center of the Sun is 15,000,000 degrees Celsius (°C). The temperature of the Sun's surface is lower, about 5,500°C. Thermonuclear reactions in the Sun's core create thermal and light energy. About 4 million kilograms (kg) of the Sun's mass is being changed into thermal and light energy every second. This energy radiates out from the Sun in all directions. A small amount of it reaches Earth.

Another name for the Sun is Sol. The solar system is named for the ruling star.

The reason the Sun rules is its size. The Sun has 99.8 percent of the total mass of the solar system. All the other solar system objects travel around the Sun in predictable, almost-circular paths called orbits. The most obvious objects orbiting the Sun are the planets.

Terrestrial Planets

The terrestrial planets are the four planets closest to the Sun. The terrestrial planets are small and rocky.

The four inner planets are small and dense, with solid rocky surfaces and few or no moons. The relative sizes of these terrestrial planets are shown here.

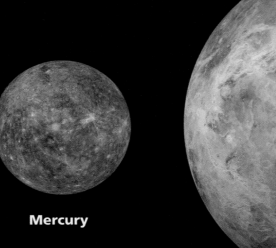

Mercury

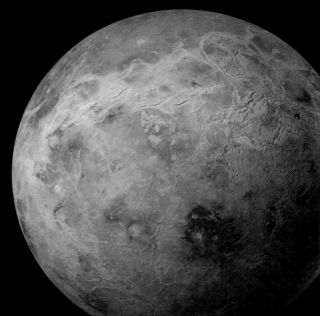

Venus

Mercury

Mercury is the closest planet to the Sun. It is smaller than Earth and has no natural satellite. By human standards, it is an uninviting place. Mercury is very hot on the side facing the Sun and very cold on the side away from the Sun. It has no atmosphere or water.

Mercury is covered with craters. The craters are the result of thousands of collisions with objects flying through space. The surface of Mercury looks a lot like Earth's Moon.

Venus

Venus is the second planet from the Sun. It is about the same size as Earth and has no natural satellite. The surface of Venus is very hot all the time. It is one of the hottest places in the solar system. It is hot enough to melt lead!

There is no liquid water on Venus. It has an atmosphere of carbon dioxide. The dense, cloudy atmosphere makes it impossible to see the planet's surface. Modern radar, however, allows scientists to collect images through the clouds. We now know that the surface of Venus is dry and cracked, and has many volcanoes.

Earth

Mars

Earth

Earth is the third planet from the Sun. It has a moderate temperature all the time. It has an atmosphere of nitrogen and oxygen, and it has liquid water. As far as we know, Earth is the only place in the universe that has life.

Earth also has one large satellite called the Moon, or Luna. The Moon orbits Earth in about a month. The Moon is responsible for the tides in Earth's ocean. The Moon is the only extraterrestrial place humans have visited.

Earth is 150 million km from the Sun. This is a huge distance. It is hard to imagine that distance, but think about this. Sit in one end zone of a football field and curl up into a ball. You are the Sun. A friend goes to the other end zone and holds up the eraser from a pencil. That is Earth. Get the idea? Earth is tiny, and it is a long distance from the Sun. Still, the solar energy that reaches Earth provides the right amount of energy for life as we know it.

Mars

Mars is the fourth planet from the Sun and has two small satellites, Phobos and Deimos. Mars is a little like Earth, except it is smaller, colder, and drier. There are some places on Mars that are somewhat like Death Valley in California. Other places on Mars are more like Antarctica and the volcanoes of Hawaii.

The Mars rover Spirit is one of several robotic craft that have explored the Red Planet. This composite image of rippled sand deposits lining a crater, taken by Spirit, shows the reddish color of the planet's surface.

Mars is sometimes called the Red Planet because of its red soil. The soil contains iron oxide, or rust. The iron oxide in the soil tells scientists that Mars probably had liquid water at one time. But liquid water has not been on Mars for 3.5 billion years. It has frozen water in polar ice caps that grow and shrink with the seasons.

Mars is the next likely place humans will visit. But exploring Mars will not be easy. Humans cannot breathe the thin atmosphere of carbon dioxide. Astronauts will need to wear life-support space suits for protection against the cold.

Several robotic landers have explored Mars and sent back information about the surface. In 2008, the Phoenix Mars Lander confirmed the presence of ice and water vapor in the soil. The *Mars Reconnaissance Orbiter* has returned images of a constantly changing Martian surface.

Asteroids

Beyond the orbit of Mars, there are millions of chunks of rock and iron called asteroids. They all orbit the Sun in a region called the asteroid belt. The asteroid belt is like the boundary of the terrestrial planets. When the spacecraft *Galileo* flew past asteroid Ida in 1993, scientists were surprised to find that it had a satellite. They named the tiny moon Dactyl. The biggest asteroid is Ceres. It is about 960 km in diameter. Ceres is also called a dwarf planet.

These layered deposits on a valley floor on Mars' surface may be evidence of liquid water in the planet's distant past.

Jupiter

Gas Giant Planets

The next four planets are the gas giant planets, which are made mostly of gas. They do not have rocky surfaces like the terrestrial planets. So there is no place to land or walk around on them. They are much bigger than the terrestrial planets. What we have learned about the gas giant planets has come from probes sent out to fly by and orbit them. Even though the gas giant planets are all made of gas, each one is different.

Jupiter

Jupiter is the fifth planet from the Sun. It is the largest planet in the solar system. It is 11 times larger in diameter than Earth.

Scientists have found evidence of at least 67 moons orbiting Jupiter. The four largest moons, Io, Europa, Ganymede, and Callisto, were first described by Galileo Galilei (1564–1642) in 1610.

Jupiter's atmosphere is cold and poisonous. It is mostly hydrogen and helium. The stripes and swirls on Jupiter's surface are cold, windy clouds of ammonia and water. Its Great Red Spot is a giant storm as wide as three Earths. This storm has been going on for hundreds of years. On Jupiter, the atmospheric pressure is so strong that it squishes gas into liquid. Jupiter's atmosphere could crush a metal spaceship like a paper cup.

Uranus

Neptune

Saturn

The four outer planets are very large, made up mostly of gases, and have rings and many moons. The relative sizes of these gas giants are shown here, but the scale is different than the album of terrestrial planets on pages 88–89. Can you use the image on pages 86–87 to determine the relative scale?

Saturn

Saturn is the sixth planet from the Sun. It is the second largest planet and is very cold. There is evidence of at least 62 moons orbiting Saturn. Saturn is made up mostly of hydrogen, helium, and methane. It does not have a solid surface. It has clouds and storms like Jupiter, but they are harder to see because they move so fast. Winds in Saturn's upper atmosphere reach 1,825 km per hour.

The most dramatic feature of Saturn is its ring system. The largest ring reaches out 200,000 km from Saturn's surface. The rings are made of billions of small chunks of ice and rock that are spaced fairly far apart. All the gas giant planets have rings, but the others are not as spectacular as Saturn's.

Uranus

Uranus is the seventh planet from the Sun. There is evidence of at least 27 moons and 13 rings orbiting Uranus. Uranus is very cold and windy, and would be poisonous to humans. It is smaller and colder than Saturn.

Uranus has clouds that are extremely cold at the top. Below the cloud tops, there is a layer of water, ammonia, and methane. Like other gas giant planets, Uranus may be very hot at its core. Uranus appears blue because of the methane gas in its atmosphere.

The *New Horizons* spacecraft was the first to explore Pluto. It flew around Pluto from July 2015 through October 2016, obtaining detailed images of Pluto's surface for the first time. Pluto is slightly smaller than Earth's Moon.

Neptune

Neptune is the eighth planet from the Sun. There is evidence of at least 13 moons and 5 thin rings orbiting Neptune. Neptune is the smallest of the gas giant planets, but is still larger than the terrestrial planets.

Neptune is made mostly of hydrogen and helium with some methane. It might be the windiest planet in the solar system. Winds rip through the clouds at more than 2,000 km per hour. Scientists think there might be an ocean of extremely hot water under Neptune's cold clouds. It does not boil away because of the incredible pressure on the planet.

The Kuiper Belt

Out beyond the giant planets are asteroids, comets, and icy objects in the Kuiper Belt. Some of the objects are big enough to be dwarf planets. Others have orbits that send them flying through the rest of the solar system.

Pluto

Pluto is one of the Kuiper Belt objects. Scientists used to consider Pluto a planet. It is massive enough for its gravity to shape it into a sphere. But as astronomers learned more about the outer solar system, they realized it is similar to other large pieces of debris in the Kuiper Belt. Scientists now classify Pluto as a **plutoid**, a type of dwarf planet.

The Sun would look like a bright star from faraway Eris. Compare this to our own view of the Sun every day.

Pluto has a thin atmosphere. It is so cold that the atmosphere actually freezes and falls to Pluto's surface when it is farthest from the Sun. Even though Pluto is smaller than Earth's Moon, it has its own satellites. They are named Charon, Nix, and Hydra.

Eris

In July 2005, astronomers at the California Institute of Technology announced the discovery of a new planet-like object. It is called Eris. Like Pluto, Eris is a Kuiper Belt object and a dwarf planet. But Eris is more than twice as far away from the Sun as Pluto is! The picture above gives an artist's idea of what the Sun would look like from a position close to Eris.

Comets

Sometimes comets are compared to dirty snowballs. Scientists think comets might provide valuable information about the origins of the solar system.

Comets orbit the Sun in long, oval paths. Most of them travel far beyond the orbit of Pluto. A comet's trip around the Sun can take hundreds or even millions of years, depending on its orbit. A comet's tail shows up as it nears the Sun and begins to warm. The gases and dust that form the comet's tail always point away from the Sun.

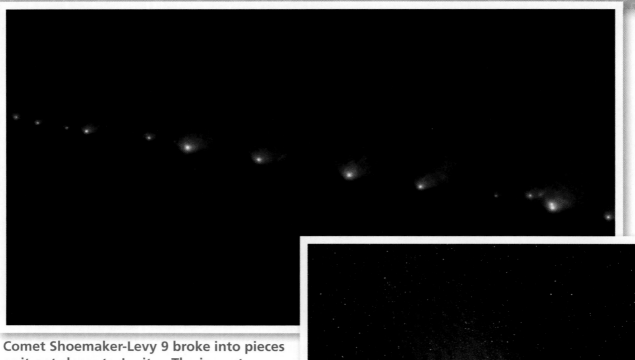

Comet Shoemaker-Levy 9 broke into pieces as it got closer to Jupiter. The impact was the first collision between two solar system objects ever to be observed.

Unlike rocky asteroids, comets are chunks of ice, dust, and frozen gases. They have been called dirty snowballs.

Comets' orbits can cross those of the planets. In July 1994, a large comet, named Comet Shoemaker-Levy 9, was on a collision course with Jupiter. As it got close to Jupiter, the comet broke into more than 20 pieces. The pieces slammed into Jupiter for a week, and the impacts were observed closely by astronomers on Earth. Each impact created a crater larger than Earth in Jupiter's surface.

The Stardust mission collected particles from Comet Wild 2 and returned them to Earth in 2006. Scientists have been studying these particles for years to understand more about the composition and origin of comets. In 2011, they found evidence of liquid water in the particles, causing them to question under what circumstances comets may partially melt.

Think Questions

1. What is the Sun, and what is it made of?
2. What is the solar system?
3. Which planets are terrestrial planets? Which planets are gas giant planets?
4. What is found in the Kuiper Belt?

Earth's Changing Systems

From space, Earth looks like a lovely blue and white marble. This relatively small planet is the only place we know that can sustain life.

Earth's Resources

With a population of 7.4 billion humans and countless other organisms, Earth is unique. Earth's residents all have requirements for life. All living organisms must eat food and drink water. They exchange gases such as oxygen and carbon dioxide. Organisms obtain these resources from Earth's systems: the biosphere, hydrosphere, atmosphere, and geosphere.

Liquid water is essential for all living things. Earth has abundant water, making our planet uniquely suitable for life. But protecting this resource is a challenge.

Humans are just one part of the biosphere, but we affect Earth's resources in unique ways. We can invent and build like no other species on the planet. We can use agriculture, water purification, health care, transportation, communication, and construction to make life last longer. All these technologies require resources from Earth, such as **fossil fuels**, minerals, and building materials.

As more humans live longer, our population is rapidly increasing. This increase leads to a problem. As the human population increases, demands for basic resources, materials, and fuel also increase. We demand more and more from the Earth systems that provide these resources.

The Atmosphere

Earth's atmosphere provides oxygen for aerobic organisms, such as humans. It provides carbon dioxide for photosynthetic organisms, such as plants. Organisms release gases into the atmosphere during respiration. They are part of a natural cycle of life-sustaining gases.

Some human activities, however, affect the balance of the atmosphere. Humans are increasing the level of carbon dioxide in the atmosphere in two important ways.

Human resource use, such as burning fossil fuels to meet energy demands, affects Earth's systems. As human population increases, we need more resources.

Fossil fuel use. We burn fossil fuels such as coal, oil, natural gas, and gasoline. These fuels come from underground sources that took millions of years to form. When we burn them, we release carbon dioxide into the atmosphere. Humans burn fossil fuels to power cars, airplanes, and trains. We use them to generate electricity that run businesses and homes—essential parts of our lives.

Tree removal. Trees convert carbon dioxide in the atmosphere into sugars and cellulose that they use for growth. But humans often cut down forests to use the land or wood. Fewer growing trees mean less photosynthesis, and the carbon dioxide in the atmosphere increases.

Why is carbon dioxide a big deal? It is one of several **greenhouse gases**. These gases "trap" energy in the atmosphere. They cause it to stay warm, like a greenhouse. Greenhouse gases are important. They keep Earth's temperature stable and warm enough to permit life. But as humans add more greenhouse gases to the atmosphere, its temperature keeps increasing. This rise in temperature produces climate change. And that change affects weather patterns that result in more severe weather.

Humans cut down trees to use the wood, or to clear the land for farming or residential use.

0 ft sea level rise

2 ft sea level rise

A computer model shows how a 0.6-meter (2-foot) sea-level rise would impact the San Francisco Bay Area. Low-lying areas (in green on the left) would be underwater (in blue on the right).

The Hydrosphere

As we have seen, water is essential for life on Earth. As our population increases, so does our need for fresh water. We often take water from streams or rivers, moving it to cities and farms. This water use can leave other parts of the **ecosystem** without enough water to sustain local species.

In other cases, humans create pollution that ends up in the water. This happens when fertilizer washes off farmlands, when plastic trash is dumped into a stream, or when waste water flows into a river. Water flows downhill to lakes or the ocean, carrying the pollution with it.

Most of Earth's fresh water is solid, frozen in ice packs near the North Pole or South Pole. As Earth's climate warms, these ice packs melt. Scientists use computer models to predict how quickly the climate will change and the ice will melt. The complex models indicate that sea levels will rise significantly. Some coastal areas are expected to disappear under water over the next several decades. As the cold, fresh meltwater flows into the saltwater ocean, it disrupts ocean currents. This in turn affects ocean ecosystems and weather patterns on land.

When polluted water is released into a stream, it enters the hydrosphere. The water can flow to a river, lake, or the ocean, carrying the pollution along with it.

The Geosphere

Digging into Earth's crust is a common way to get resources. Humans mine materials such as gravel and clay, metals such as gold and silver, and fossil fuels such as gas and coal. Wells pull oil from the ground. As the human population increases, demand for these materials increases. Humans invent more difficult ways to get the remaining resources. A technology called **fracking** injects liquids into the ground to force oil out. And in some locations, whole mountaintops are removed to get coal.

Getting these resources from Earth is necessary to make modern conveniences. They let us travel in cars that run on gasoline. But burning gasoline and other fossil fuels releases more carbon dioxide into the atmosphere.

Mining operations affect Earth's systems. Wastewater from mines and fracking sites contains toxic minerals and other pollutants. These can contaminate water sources. Humans try to use safe mining and oil drilling practices. But accidents can pollute nearby ecosystems and harm the organisms who live there.

The Biosphere

Humans use many organisms in the biosphere as resources. We use wood for construction and paper. We take materials from plants and animals for food and clothing. Sometimes humans remove a large part of an ecosystem to plant crops or build structures. These human actions change ecosystems dramatically. As the human population grows, many other species are threatened with extinction.

Population Growth and Resources

Scientists are questioning how many humans this planet can support. As Earth's population of humans and our need for resources grow, many scientists and engineers are looking for ways to get resources without harming other Earth systems. Part of the solution relies on changing our behavior. For example, water conservation and modern irrigation practices decrease the impact of human water use on local ecosystems.

Energy use is one of our greatest resource challenges. Fossil fuels are a relatively inexpensive energy source that humans can use. But fossil fuels took hundreds of millions of years to form, and we are using them up more rapidly than they can form. They are **nonrenewable** energy sources. And fossil fuels are a problem because of their role in climate change.

Can food production keep pace with population growth? To achieve sustainable food systems, large and small farming operations around the world must become efficient and ecologically sensitive.

Global population grows by about 200,000 every day, or more than 70 million each year. No wonder there is tension between our expanding needs and what the planet can provide.

Do you remember the definition of a system? It is a collection of interacting parts. In climate change, Earth's systems are all interacting. Computer models help scientists explore how changes to one system might affect another. When humans release carbon dioxide in the atmosphere by burning fossil fuels from the geosphere, Earth's climate changes. Climate affects storms, temperature, and precipitation patterns (hydrosphere). These in turn affect every living thing in the biosphere.

The Future on Earth

Scientists mark Earth's history by significant events, including major extinctions. Today's significant events result from rapidly increasing human population and resource use. Humans are changing the planet so much that some scientists think we have entered a new age. They call it the **anthropocene**. *Anthropo* means human, and *cene* indicates a new geologic age.

Wind power is a clean and renewable energy resource. Wind turbines like these transfer the kinetic energy of the wind into electrical energy.

The good news is that humans are creative and intelligent. We can use those qualities to solve tough problems. For example, we are developing more ways to harness **renewable** energy sources. When we use solar, geothermal, and wind power, we burn less fossil fuel. With 7.4 billion people and counting, it may not feel like your decisions make much of a difference. But when you add up the decisions that each person makes, we can make a big difference. Together, we can choose to care for the planet, which we share with all life.

Think Questions

1. **What are some examples of one Earth system interacting with another?**
2. **What are some ways in which humans are changing Earth's systems?**
3. **Why is climate change considered a global issue?**

The Hunt for Water

A rainbow after a storm is a beautiful sight. But more than just a pretty sky, it also reveals information about the kinds of light that make up what we call white light from the Sun.

A **spectroscope** can break light into its various **wavelengths** just like the water droplets of a rainbow. Have you used a spectroscope to look at the lights around you? If so, the spectra for incandescent and fluorescent lights might look familiar. The different patterns of color reveal what elements or compounds are emitting the light.

A rainbow forms when water droplets bend and separate visible white light from the Sun into its many wavelengths, or colors.

Incandescent light shows an even spread of rainbow colors. This **spectrum** comes from a white-hot filament in a lightbulb. The filament is made of tungsten, a rare metal. The Sun's spectrum looks very much like this, but is very bright.

Fluorescent light shows bright color lines standing out against a dimmer spectrum. The main bright lines come from the element mercury.

Imagine you are on a NASA (National Aeronautics and Space Administration) mission to find water in the solar system. The problem is, you cannot go there to get samples. How can you study faraway places, like moons, planets, and stars? You can get information from the light they emit or reflect. Two simple properties of light can provide powerful information. They are the light's brightness and color.

Colors of **visible light** range from red (low energy, long wavelengths) to violet (high energy, short wavelengths). Shorter wavelengths than violet are invisible to us. They include ultraviolet light, X-rays, and gamma rays. Longer wavelengths than red are also invisible to us. They include infrared light, microwaves, and radio waves.

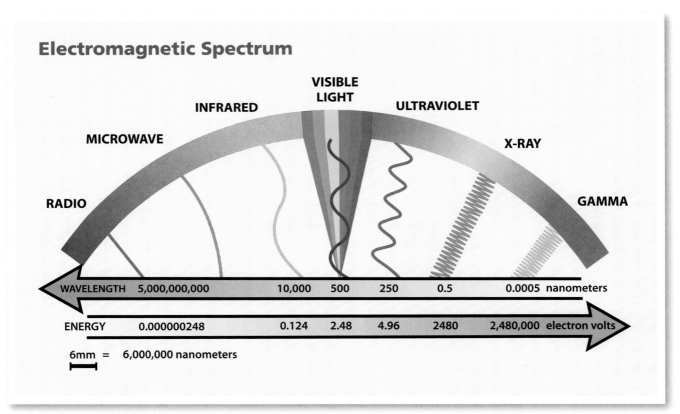

Electromagnetic Spectrum

MICROWAVE   INFRARED   VISIBLE LIGHT   ULTRAVIOLET   X-RAY

RADIO   GAMMA

WAVELENGTH	5,000,000,000		10,000	500	250	0.5	0.0005	nanometers
ENERGY	0.000000248		0.124	2.48	4.96	2480	2,480,000	electron volts

6mm = 6,000,000 nanometers

The wavelengths of light we can see make up the visible spectrum, a small part of the entire electromagnetic spectrum. Longer and shorter wavelengths are detectable only with tools like a spectroscope.

Seeing the Invisible

Human eyes can see wavelengths only of certain sizes. Hydrogen emits light at wavelengths that we cannot see, even with our spectroscope. These wavelengths are in the ultraviolet region of the **electromagnetic spectrum**. However, there are tools to detect the wavelengths that our eyes cannot see. For example, some space probes detect gamma rays, which are not in the visible spectrum. We would not see anything, even with a telescope or classroom spectroscope. But tools designed to detect gamma rays can observe powerful energy from a supernova.

Every element and compound is unique. Each has a unique spectral signature. Much like fingerprints, the spectral signature can be used to identify elements and compounds.

Consider hydrogen, one of the two elements in water molecules. There are two ways to analyze its spectral signature.

Emission lines. Hydrogen atoms emit light of specific wavelengths. Bright lines show the wavelength of the emitted light.

Absorption lines. When white light passes through a substance containing hydrogen, the element absorbs certain wavelengths of light. The **absorption lines** occur in the same places as the **emission lines**, but will appear as dark bands.

Take Note

What part of the electromagnetic spectrum could you analyze using the spectroscope? Write your answer in your notebook.

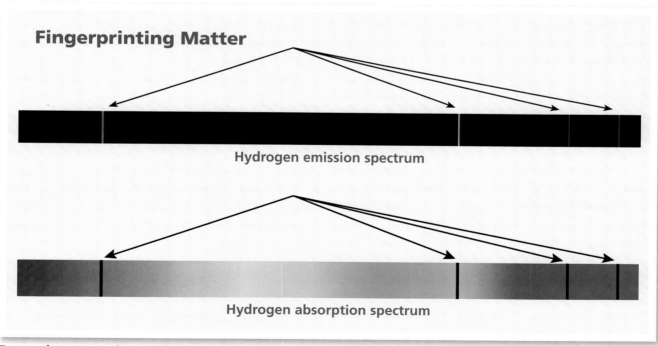

Every element emits a unique wavelength of light. This characteristic light spectrum helps identify it in samples of unknown substances. The science of examining the pattern of lines and colors and comparing them to those of known elements is called spectroscopy.

Spectral Signature of Water

Hydrogen and oxygen are the elements in water. A spectroscope, however, shows far more lines for water vapor (gas) than for either oxygen or hydrogen alone. The spectrum is more complex because hydrogen and oxygen formed a compound called water.

We do see strong hydrogen lines in the spectrum. If we look carefully, we can pick out oxygen lines. But much of the spectrum of water is outside the visible spectrum. We cannot see these infrared and microwave wavelengths. Scientists need powerful tools to detect these wavelengths and confirm the presence of water.

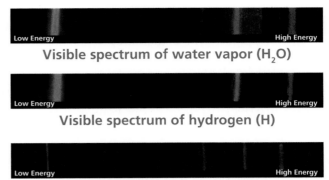

Low Energy   High Energy

Visible spectrum of water vapor (H_2O)

Low Energy   High Energy

Visible spectrum of hydrogen (H)

Low Energy   High Energy

Visible spectrum of oxygen (O_2)

When you analyze the spectrum of water vapor (H_2O), you can see similarities to the spectra of each element that makes up water, hydrogen (H) and oxygen (O).

We see water as a clear, colorless liquid. A spectroscope "sees" water—actually, water vapor—in terms of its chemical makeup, or atomic structure.

The *Juno* probe is orbiting Jupiter for a year, gathering data about its atmosphere and other features. Astronomers believe Jupiter has much to teach us about our solar system and its formation.

Water on Jupiter

Scientists are debating the origin and early development of the solar system. They try to gather information to support their ideas. Jupiter, the largest of the planets, holds answers to questions about the formation of the solar system. The primary goal of NASA's Juno mission is to help us understand Jupiter's structure, formation, and evolution. That includes searching Jupiter for water. *Juno* launched in August 2011 and arrived at Jupiter to start collecting data in July 2016.

Juno began measuring water right away using an instrument called a **radiometer**. It detects microwave emissions. Those are the same kind of energy used in microwave ovens. The radiometer measures the abundance of hydrogen in Jupiter's atmosphere. From this observation, scientists can infer the amount of water in Jupiter's atmosphere.

The Juno mission may help reveal how the solar system formed. The conditions that produced the Milky Way galaxy and the solar system also produced life on Earth. Using data from the mission to Jupiter, scientists will try to understand those conditions and their importance in the origin of the human species.

Think Questions

1. **We have not visited Jupiter to collect samples, so how do we know what the atmosphere is composed of?**

2. **What do scientists hope to learn from the Juno mission?**

Finding Exoplanets

Eight planets orbit our star. With an estimated 200 billion stars in the Milky Way galaxy and 100 billion galaxies in the universe, how many planets might be out there?

Finding a planet circling a star other than the Sun is not easy. Such planets are called **exoplanets**. Finding them presents two problems.

Problem 1. Other stars are very far away. Suppose a star is only 33 light-years (ly) away. That is a fairly close star, but it's about 330,000,000,000,000 kilometers (km) away. Looking for a planet the size of Earth that far away is like trying to see a person's nose 20 km away. Our most powerful telescope, the Hubble Space Telescope, could do the job, except for problem 2.

Problem 2. The light coming from a star is too bright. Did you ever look for an airplane or bird flying in the direction of the Sun? You should never look directly at the Sun. But even if you tried, the intense light from the Sun would make you look away. Stars produce a huge amount of light. The light from a star overpowers any light reflected from the planet.

Because of the great distances and the stars' intense light, it is impossible to find planets by looking for them directly. Instead, we look at how stars behave by searching for stars that move back and forth slightly and stars that get slightly dimmer.

Thousands of planets have been discovered orbiting stars other than the Sun. Find out how scientists are locating these exoplanets.

The Wobble Method

The pull of gravity keeps planets in orbit around a star. This first diagram shows a planet orbiting a star.

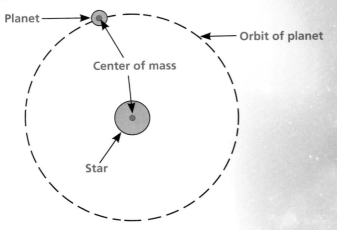

Closer analysis shows that the star's gravity pulls on the planet and the planet's gravity pulls on the star. So the planet does not orbit around the star's center of mass. Both the planet and the star orbit a common "center of gravity," or **barycenter**. This second diagram shows the planet and the star orbiting the barycenter. The star's orbit is tiny, but big enough to make the star wobble from side to side.

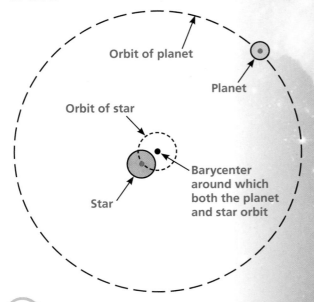

One way to locate exoplanets in the star field is to look for signs of gravitational interaction between a planet and its star.

How far off-center does the planet pull its star? If the solar system consisted of only the Sun and Jupiter, the barycenter would be just outside the Sun's surface.

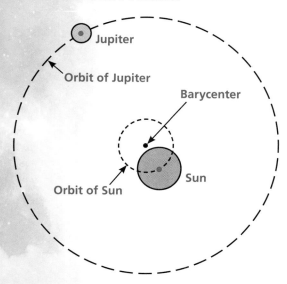

What if the solar system consisted of only the Sun and Earth? The barycenter would be deep within the Sun, but not at the center of the Sun. A larger planet causes a bigger wobble of the star, because larger planets have more gravitational pull.

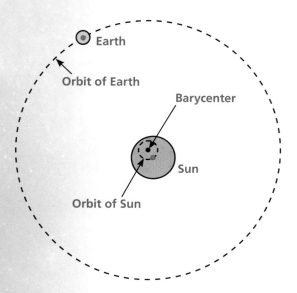

Light waves from a moving source of light—a star—change depending on whether the star and Earth are moving toward or away from each other. These shifts in the patterns of light from distant stars help astronomers locate exoplanets.

Detecting a wobble. We can detect a planet indirectly by looking for a star's wobble. The star's spectrum shifts if there is a wobble. This is how it works.

Astronomers observe the spectrum lines produced by the gases in a star. Spectrum lines show what wavelengths of light the gases emit.

The spectrum lines shift slightly when the star moves. The lines shift toward the violet end of the spectrum if the star is moving closer to us. The lines shift toward the red end if the star is moving away. This change is called the **Doppler shift**.

The Doppler shift in light waves is like hearing a siren pass by. The pitch of the siren is higher when the sound source is moving toward you. It is lower when the sound source is moving away from you.

This is an artist's concept of the first exoplanet detected around a Sun-like star, 51 Pegasi, about 50 ly away in the constellation Pegasus. About half the size of Jupiter, the planet circles the star in just 4 days.

The sound waves get pushed together as the source moves toward you. They get stretched apart as it moves away from you.

Discovering many planets. In 1996, a team of Swiss astronomers, including Michel Mayor (1942–) and Didier Queloz (1966–), used the **wobble method** to detect a possible planet. It had the same mass as Jupiter. It orbits a nearby Sun-like star called 51 Pegasi. By 2017, nearly 700 exoplanets had been discovered using this method, making up about 20 percent of all confirmed exoplanets.

The wobble method is sometimes called the spectroscopic method or radial velocity method of planet finding. The Doppler shift of spectral lines is evidence of the star's wobble. And the wobble is evidence of an exoplanet's gravitational effect on its star.

The Transit Method

If a planet passes directly in front of its star, the event is called a **transit**. During a transit, the planet blocks a small amount of the star's light. The star dims slightly, or blinks. The bigger the planet is, the bigger the drop in brightness, and the bigger the blink. Observing star blinks is the transit method of detecting exoplanets.

Observing a blink is not easy. What would an observer from another planetary system see when the largest planet, Jupiter, passes in front of the Sun? The Sun's brightness would dip by 1 percent. Earth would cause only a 0.01 percent drop in brightness, or 1 part in 10,000. Blinks are a long drop in brightness, 2 to 16 hours. But they are short compared with the time it takes the planet to orbit its star. A planet can transit its star once per orbit. By detecting several blinks, an observer can calculate the **orbital period** of the planet.

TRAPPIST-1 made headlines in 2017 when scientists discovered seven terrestrial planets orbiting the star 40 ly from Earth. This illustration shows the possible view from the surface of one exoplanet with another in transit.

By 2017, more than 2,700 exoplanets had been discovered using this method, making up about 80 percent of all confirmed exoplanets. The main source of transit data in recent years has been the highly successful NASA Kepler mission. Kepler launched in March 2009, and has discovered more than 2,300 exoplanets using the transit method.

 Visit FOSSweb for an update on these numbers.

Life on Exoplanets

The discovery of exoplanets raises an interesting question. Is anything living on any of those planets?

NASA's Kepler mission is the first to look for Earth-sized and smaller planets around other stars. Kepler uses the transit method to find small planets (one-half to twice the size of Earth) in the Milky Way. It focuses on the habitable zone, the area around a star where liquid water (and possibly life) might exist. Kepler's results will allow us to estimate how many stars in the Milky Way have planets that could support life.

Kepler scientists have been observing about 100,000 stars since 2009. They collect data about the *period* (time per cycle) of the brightness drop, the *duration* of the brightness drop, and the *consistency* of the change in brightness, to confirm that a planet has been

Three of the seven TRAPPIST-1 system planets are in the habitable zone. This illustration imagines the possible surface of one of these planets, with rocky landforms and liquid water.

discovered. Then the Kepler team uses the data to estimate the radius of the planet's orbit and the mass of the star. The size of the planet is determined from the brightness drop of the star and the size of the star. They combine these data with the temperature of the star to calculate the planet's probable temperature. And that temperature indicates whether the planet *could* be inhabited.

Life in the Universe

The universe is a large study site. Scientists looking for planets focus their attention on stars within a few dozen to 3,000 ly from Earth. The Milky Way alone has at least 200 billion stars. They are in a spinning disk that is about 100,000 ly across and 10,000 ly thick. The vast majority of the stars in the Milky Way are too far away to search for planets.

Beyond the Milky Way, the universe has countless other galaxies. Each galaxy has billions of stars. Some of the galaxies are like ours, a disk with starry arms reaching out. Others are elliptical or irregular. The distances between galaxies, even those in the Local Group, are too great to search for planets outside the Milky Way.

But we know that planets do orbit other stars. There could be many other worlds like Earth. Somewhere out there, at this very moment, there could be students in classrooms on other planets wondering . . . is there life anywhere else in the universe?

Think Questions

1. Once we confirm other planetary systems, what do you think the next stage of exploration should be?

2. Why don't we have a photo of the entire Milky Way, like those of the galaxies on this page?

Astronomers studying our ever-changing universe can use infrared light to examine the dust clouds where new stars are being born. Young stars glow red, while the rest of this galaxy's billions of stars form a blue haze.

Images and Data

Images and Data   Table of Contents

White House

White House Neighborhood

White House Community

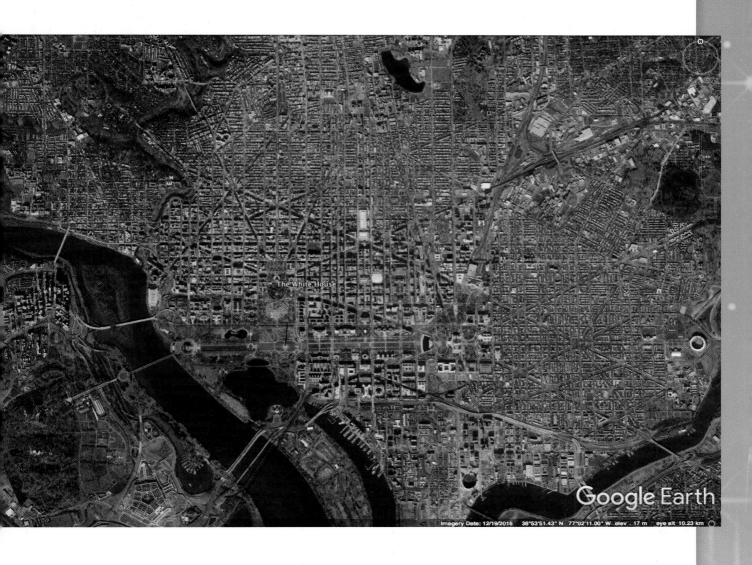

Washington, DC, Area

Northeast Region

The White House

Image Landsat / Copernicus
Data SIO, NOAA, U.S. Navy, NGA, GEBCO

Google Earth

Imagery Date: 12/13/2015   38°53'51.38" N   77°02'11.01" W elev 67 m   eye alt 1001.45 km

Earth

Image Landsat / Copernicus
Data SIO, NOAA, U.S. Navy, NGA, GEBCO
Image IBCAO
Image U.S. Geological Survey

Google Earth

eylt 12lt 1243.52 krm

Worldwide Sunrise/Sunset Data

June 21

City and country	Latitude	Sunrise	Sunset	Length of day
Barrow, AK, USA	71° N	None	None	24:00
Stockholm, Sweden	59° N	2:48	8:59	18:11
Sendai, Japan	38° N	4:18	7:06	14:48
Alexandria, VA, USA	38° N	5:44	8:37	14:53
New Delhi, India	28° N	5:22	7:18	13:56
Quito, Ecuador	0°	6:22	6:22	12:00
Nairobi, Kenya	1° S	6:34	6:34	12:00
Auckland, New Zealand	37° S	7:48	4:55	9:07
Punta Arenas, Chile	53° S	8:00	3:32	7:32

December 21

City and country	Latitude	Sunrise	Sunset	Length of day
Barrow, AK, USA	71° N	None	None	0:00
Stockholm, Sweden	59° N	9:53	4:03	6:10
Sendai, Japan	38° N	7:00	4:32	9:32
Alexandria, VA, USA	38° N	7:23	4:50	9:27
New Delhi, India	28° N	7:03	5:31	10:28
Quito, Ecuador	0°	6:14	6:22	12:08
Nairobi, Kenya	1° S	6:24	6:35	12:11
Auckland, New Zealand	37° S	4:56	7:37	14:41
Punta Arenas, Chile	53° S	3:50	8:46	16:56

Think Questions

1. Which locations have the most hours of daylight on June 21? The fewest hours of daylight?

2. Which locations have the most hours of daylight on December 21? The fewest hours of daylight?

3. Alpena, Michigan, is at latitude 45° north. How much daylight do you estimate it has on June 21? On December 21?

4. Boulder, Colorado, is at latitude 40° north. Wellington, New Zealand, is at latitude 41° south. Which city has the most daylight on June 21?

Full Moon

Moon Image

Earth/Moon Comparison

Sun, Planets, and Satellites in the Solar System

Name   Name of planet or satellite   **Radius**   Radius of planet or satellite (in kilometers)

Orbits   The body it orbits   **Density**   Grams per cubic centimeter

Distance   Distance to the body   **Orbital period**   Time to complete orbit (in Earth days)

       it orbits (in 1,000 km)   **Rotational period**   Time to complete rotation (in Earth days)

Name	Orbits	Distance (1,000 km)	Radius (km)	Density (g/cm^3)	Orbital period	Rotational period
Sun	—	—	695,000	1.41	—	25–36
Mercury	Sun	57,910	2,440	5.42	88.0	59.0
Venus	Sun	108,200	6,052	5.25	225.0	−243.0
Earth	Sun	149,600	6,378	5.515	365.26	1.0
Moon	Earth	384	1,737	3.34	29.5	29.5
Mars	Sun	227,940	3,390	3.94	687.0	1.0
Phobos	Mars	9	14 × 11*	2.0	0.3	0.3
Deimos	Mars	23	8 × 6*	1.7	1.3	1.3
Jupiter	Sun	778,330	71,492	1.33	4,333.0	0.4
Io	Jupiter	422	1,815	3.55	1.8	1.8
Europa	Jupiter	671	1,561	3.01	3.6	3.6
Ganymede	Jupiter	1,070	2,631	1.94	7.0	7.0
Callisto	Jupiter	1,883	2,410	1.86	16.7	16.7
Saturn	Sun	1,429,400	60,268	0.69	10,760.0	0.4
Epimetheus	Saturn	151	72 × 54*	0.7	0.7	0.7
Janus	Saturn	151	98 × 96*	0.67	0.7	0.7
Mimas	Saturn	186	196	1.17	1.0	1.0
Enceladus	Saturn	238	250	1.24	1.4	1.4
Tethys	Saturn	295	533	1.21	1.9	1.9
Dione	Saturn	377	560	1.43	2.7	2.7
Rhea	Saturn	527	765	1.33	4.5	4.5
Titan	Saturn	1,222	2,575	1.88	16.0	16.0
Iapetus	Saturn	3,561	730	1.21	79.0	79.0
Uranus	Sun	2,870,990	25,559	1.29	30,685.0	−0.7
Miranda	Uranus	130	236	1.15	1.4	1.4
Ariel	Uranus	191	579	1.56	2.5	2.5
Umbriel	Uranus	266	585	1.52	4.0	4.0
Titania	Uranus	436	789	1.7	8.7	8.7
Oberon	Uranus	583	775	1.64	13.5	13.4
Neptune	Sun	4,501,200	24,622	1.64	60,190.0	0.7
Triton	Neptune	355	1,350	2.07	−5.9	−5.9

* This measurement is length × width because this satellite is not a sphere.

Moonrise/Sunrise Data

Moonrise and sunrise times for January 2027 for Berkeley, California

Date	Moonrise	Sunrise	Phase
January 1	2:01 a.m.	7:25 a.m.	
January 2	3:04 a.m.	7:25 a.m.	
January 3	4:07 a.m.	7:25 a.m.	
January 4	5:07 a.m.	7:25 a.m.	
January 5	6:02 a.m.	7:25 a.m.	
January 6	6:52 a.m.	7:25 a.m.	
January 7	7:35 a.m.	7:25 a.m.	New Moon
January 8	8:12 a.m.	7:25 a.m.	
January 9	8:43 a.m.	7:25 a.m.	
January 10	9:10 a.m.	7:25 a.m.	
January 11	9:34 a.m.	7:25 a.m.	
January 12	9:57 a.m.	7:24 a.m.	
January 13	10:19 a.m.	7:24 a.m.	
January 14	10:43 a.m.	7:24 a.m.	
January 15	11:09 p.m.	7:24 a.m.	First quarter
January 16	11:40 a.m.	7:23 a.m.	
January 17	12:18 p.m.	7:23 a.m.	
January 18	1:05 p.m.	7:23 a.m.	
January 19	2:05 p.m.	7:22 a.m.	
January 20	3:17 p.m.	7:22 a.m.	
January 21	4:34 p.m.	7:21 a.m.	
January 22	5:55 p.m.	7:21 a.m.	Full Moon
January 23	7:13 p.m.	7:20 a.m.	
January 24	8:26 p.m.	7:19 a.m.	
January 25	9:36 p.m.	7:19 a.m.	
January 26	10:44 p.m.	7:18 a.m.	
January 27	11:50 p.m.	7:17 a.m.	
January 28		7:17 a.m.	
January 29	12:55 a.m.	7:16 a.m.	Third quarter
January 30	1:58 a.m.	7:15 a.m.	
January 31	3:00 a.m.	7:14 a.m.	

Phases of the Moon Sequence Puzzle

Starting with the full Moon, put the images in order to show the sequence of the phases of the Moon.

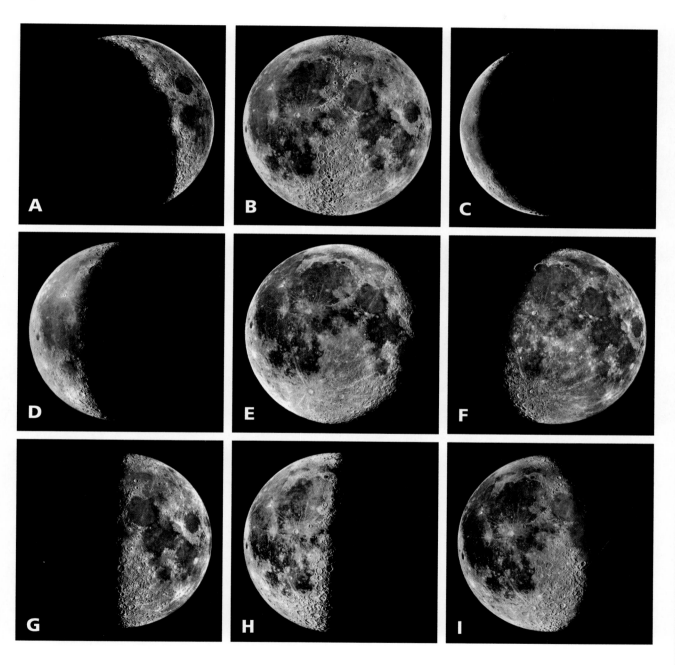

Archimedes

Aristillus

Lunar Alps

Copernicus

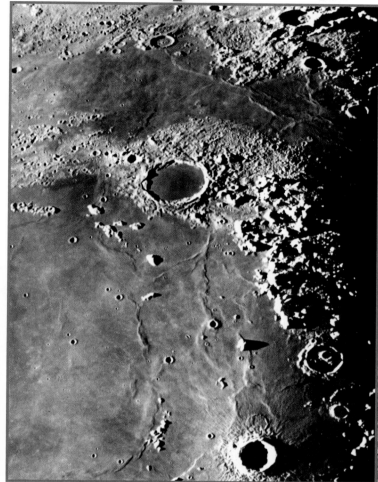

Sea of Serenity

Posidonius

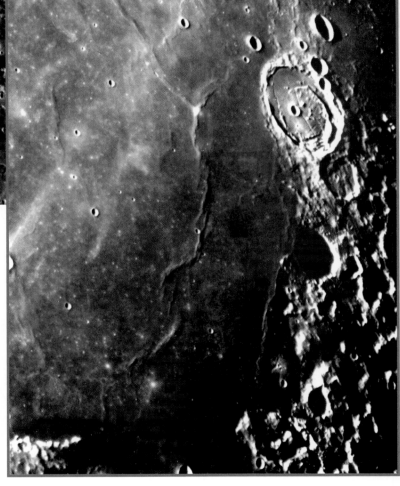

Stöfler

Tycho and Clavius

Barringer Crater, Arizona

Gosses Bluff, Australia

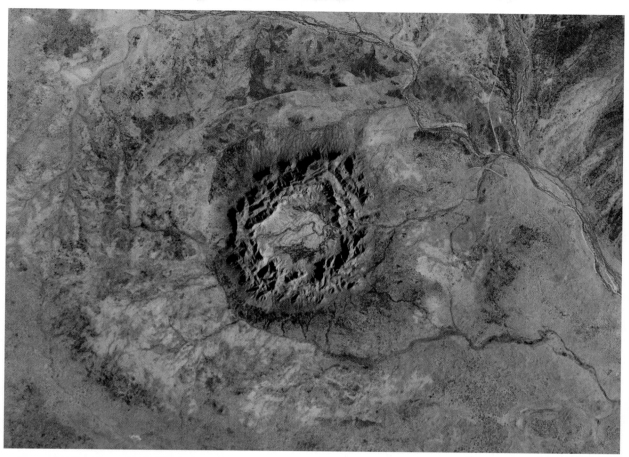

Manicouagan Crater, Canada

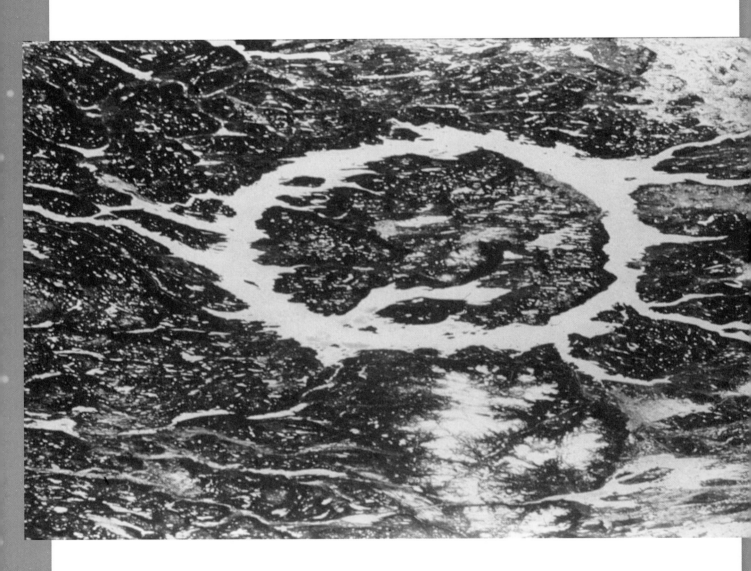

Landforms of the United States

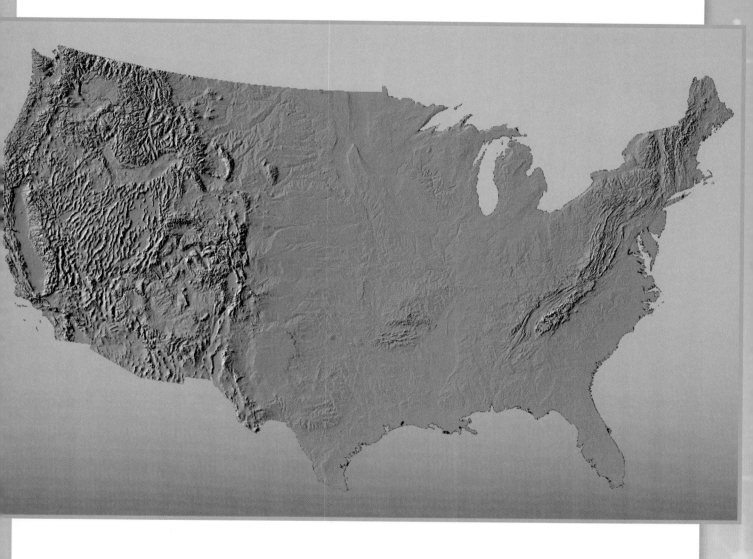

Earth Landforms, Satellite Images

A. Brazil

C. Chile

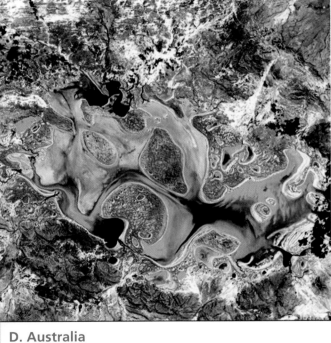

B. Brazil

D. Australia

E. Louisiana, USA

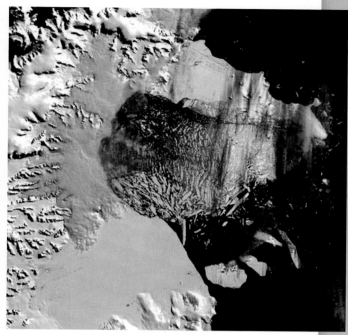

F. Antarctica

G. Washington, USA

H. Egypt

I. Argentina

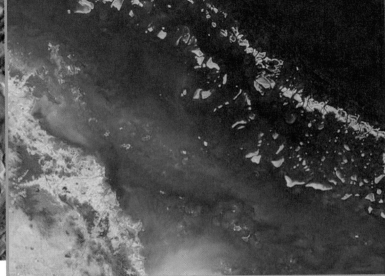

J. Australia

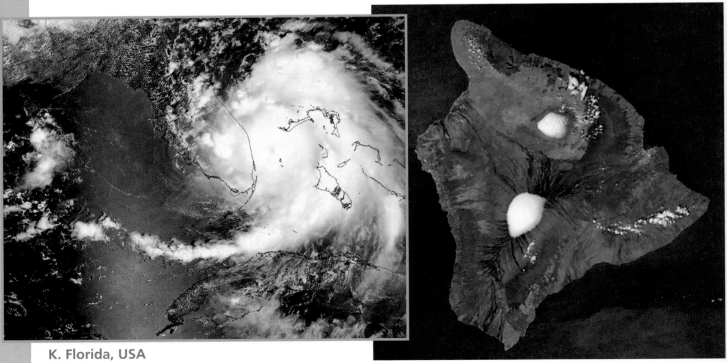

K. Florida, USA

L. Hawaii, USA

M. Venezuela

N. California, USA

O. USA and Canada

P. Tibet

Earth Landforms, Descriptions

A. Brazil

The riverbed for a meandering river is constantly shifting position as water flows. The turns in this riverbed create islands that the next flood might cover. This image of a river in Brazil was taken from the International Space Station from an altitude of 383 km.

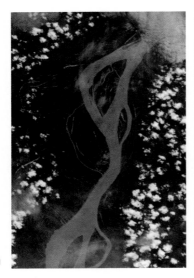

B. Brazil

Close to the city of Manaus, Brazil, the Rio Solimões and Rio Negro converge to form the Amazon River. Manaus is the gray patch to the right of the image's center.

The water of the Rio Solimões is pale and murky. It carries glacial silt and sand from its origin in the Peruvian Andes. The dark color of the Rio Negro is a feature of clear waters that carry little sediment and come from areas of exposed bedrock. East of Manaus, the pale and dark waters flow side by side before they eventually merge. Northwest of Manaus, on the Rio Negro, is the Anavilhanas archipelago, the largest group of freshwater islands in the world.

C. Chile

Chiliques volcano in Chile was thought to be dormant for 10,000 years. However, satellite data has revealed active hotspots in the crater.

Chiliques is a stratovolcano. Its circular summit crater is at 5,778 m elevation. The crater is 500 m in diameter. This mountain is one of the most important high-altitude centers for Inca ceremonies. People rarely visit it because it is so hard to reach. As you climb the trails to the summit, you pass many Inca ruins. At the summit are structures used for rituals. A beautiful lagoon in the crater is almost always frozen.

D. Australia

Lake Carnegie in Western Australia fills with water only during periods of significant rainfall. In dry years, it is a muddy marsh. This false-color image combines shortwave infrared,

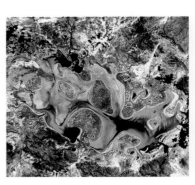

infrared, and red wavelengths.

E. Louisiana, USA

This image includes the coast of Louisiana, Mississippi, Alabama, and part of the Florida Panhandle on the Gulf of Mexico. It covers an area 345 km by 315 km. New Orleans is visible at the southern edge of Lake Pontchartrain, on the left. New Orleans is at risk of flooding. About 45 percent of the city is at or below sea level. Levees and wetlands help buffer the city from storm surges.

The Mississippi River delta, in the center, is called a bird's-foot delta because of its shape. Variations in ocean color show suspended sediment from the river and coastal areas as water flows into the Gulf. Large amounts of sediment from the land have been deposited in shallow coastal waters. These delta environments form channels and coastal wetlands that provide important habitats for waterfowl and fisheries.

F. Antarctica

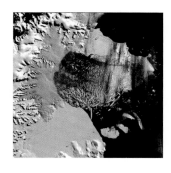

The Larsen Ice Shelf is a large, floating ice mass on the east side of the Antarctic peninsula. Antarctic ice shelves are thick plates of floating ice fed by continental glaciers. In a 35-day period beginning on January 31, 2002, about 3,250 km² of the shelf disintegrated. This event sent thousands of icebergs into the Weddell Sea. Over the next 5 years, the shelf lost a total of 5,700 km², about 60 percent of its previous size.

G. Washington, USA

Mount St. Helens in western Washington State is a stratovolcano. After lying dormant for 10,000 years, it had a major eruption on May 18, 1980. It is the most active volcano in the Cascade Range.

This image was captured on March 15, 2005, one week after an ash and steam eruption. A new lava dome in the southeast part of the crater is clearly visible. It is highlighted by red areas where a radiometer's infrared channels detected hotspots from incandescent lava. The new lava dome is 155 m higher than the old lava dome, and still growing.

H. Egypt

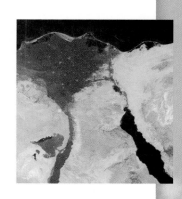

The northern portion of the Nile Delta is triangular, like the Greek letter delta, Δ. The Nile is the longest river in the world. It extends about 6,825 km from its headwaters in the highlands of eastern Africa to the Mediterranean Sea.

At the southern point of the fertile Nile Delta is Cairo, the capital of Egypt. To the west are the Great Pyramids of Giza. North of here the Nile branches into two parts, the Rosetta to the west and the Damietta to the east.

Also visible in this image is the Suez Canal, a shipping waterway connecting Port Said on the Mediterranean Sea with the Gulf of Suez. The gulf is an arm of the Red Sea, on the right.

I. Argentina

This region of the Andes Mountains is south of San Martín de Los Andes, Argentina. It shows the steep-sided valleys and other landforms carved by Pleistocene glaciers. Elevations here range from about 700 to 2,440 m. Tectonic and  volcanic activity is very common in this region. The landforms provide a record of the changes that have occurred over many thousands of years. Large lakes fill the broad mountain valleys, and the spectacular scenery makes this area a popular resort for Argentinians. What do the colors in this false-color image represent?

Answer: The colors represent different elevations. The colors from lowest to highest elevation are green, yellow, red, magenta, and white.

J. Australia

The Great Barrier Reef extends for 2,000 km along the northeastern coast of Australia. It is a vast maze of reefs, passages, and coral islands. The large island off the northernmost coast is Whitsunday Island. Smaller islands and reefs extend southeast, parallel to the coast.

This true-color image shows a portion of the southern reef, approximately 380 km wide. The reef is next to the central Queensland coast, which is the land to the west of the reef. The reef is clearly visible up to about 200 km from the coast.

K. Florida, USA

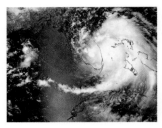

Hurricane Katrina was a relatively weak Category 1 hurricane as it approached Florida on August 24, 2005. Nine hours after it crossed the Florida peninsula, it grew to a Category 5 hurricane over the warm Gulf of Mexico waters. On August 29, this powerful hurricane struck the Louisiana coast. It caused an estimated $81 billion in damages and killed at least 1,836 people.

Outlines of Florida, the Bahamas, and the Gulf coastline have been added to this image.

L. Hawaii, USA

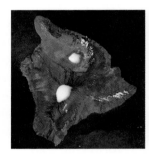

On January 14, 2005, white snow covered the summits of the high peaks of Hawaii's Mauna Loa (south) and Mauna Kea (north) volcanoes. The third volcano that makes up the island is Kilauea. Kilauea is currently active, so the lava flows give off thermal energy. The thermal energy can be detected by certain satellites (area in red).

Dark streaks of cooled and hardened lava reach down the brown slopes of the volcanoes. Lush forests grow on the lower slopes. The dots of gray around the notch in the middle of the northeast coastline are Hawaii's largest city, Hilo.

Of the three volcanoes on Hawaii, Kilauea is the most active. It started its latest eruption in 1983 and has not stopped since. Most of the volcano is covered by lava flows less than 1,000 years old. They reveal how active the volcano has been.

M. Venezuela

Duckweed plants form green swirls on the surface of Lake Maracaibo in northern Venezuela.

The lake is usually too salty for duckweed. But in 2004, unusually heavy rain brought more fresh water to the lake. The fresh water stirred the nutrient layers below. Nutrients floated to the surface, with the less dense freshwater layer on top. For a brief time, the duckweed used the nutrients to grow, and it doubled in area every day. Then the lake began to settle back into its normal layers. The nutrient-rich waters sank to the salty bottom. Without nutrients, the duckweed's growth slowed and then stopped.

N. California, USA

This image of the San Francisco Bay region shows the thermal radiation differences in urban building and road materials. The reds show hotter areas, and the greens show cooler areas. The water of the San Francisco Bay and Pacific Ocean (lower left) look black.

O. USA and Canada

The Great Lakes are the largest collection of freshwater lakes on Earth. They border Canada to the north and the

United States to the south. They formed about 10,000 years ago at the end of the last ice age. The lakes were carved out by the southern movement of large glaciers. In this mostly cloud-free image, areas with sediments flowing into the lakes are easy to see. The light color shows sediment in the southern portion of Lake Huron, Lake St. Clair, much of Lake Erie, and the outflow of the Niagara River into Lake Ontario.

P. Tibet

The Kunlun Fault is one of the gigantic strike-slip fault systems on the north side of Tibet and the Himalayas. Motion along the 1,500 km of the fault has occurred for the last 40,000 years. At a rate of 1.1 cm per year, the motion has created an offset of more than 400 m.

This image shows two faults oriented from east to west. The northern fault is marked by red lines of vegetation. The southern, younger fault cuts through the alluvial fans. Alluvial fans form when fast-flowing water from the mountains spreads out. The water drops sediments as it reaches the valley floor.

Planet Landforms, Images

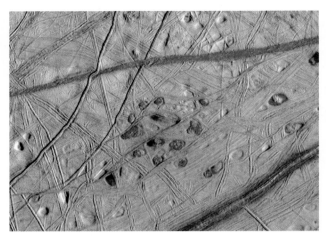

1. Jupiter's moon Europa

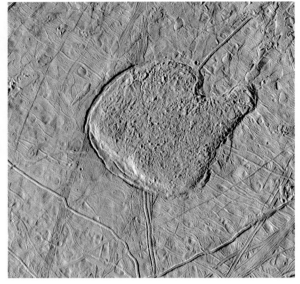

2. Jupiter's moon Europa

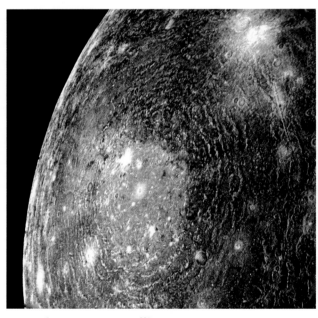

3. Jupiter's moon Callisto

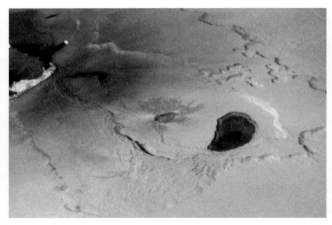

4. Jupiter's moon Io

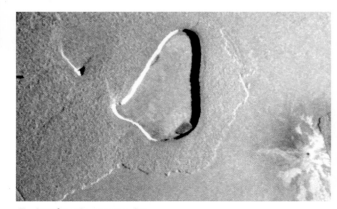

5. Jupiter's moon Io

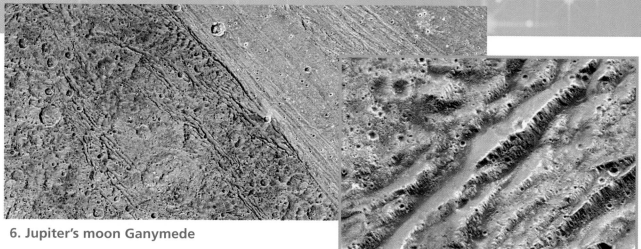

6. Jupiter's moon Ganymede

7. Ganymede close-up

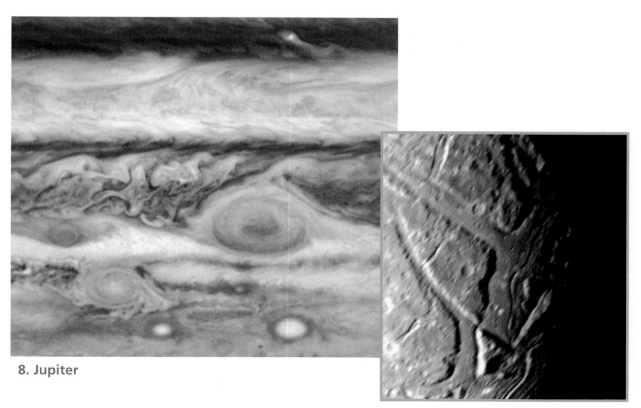

8. Jupiter

9. Uranus's moon Ariel

10. Uranus's moon Miranda

11. Saturn

12. Saturn's moon Titan

13. Saturn's moon Enceladus

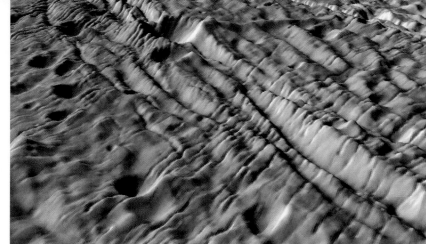

14. Neptune's moon Triton

15. Triton close-up

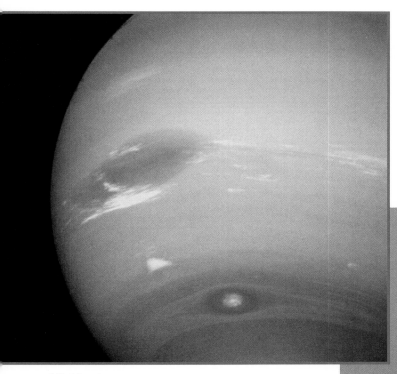

16. Neptune

17. Neptune

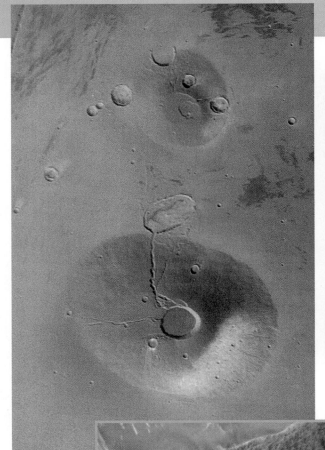

18. Mars

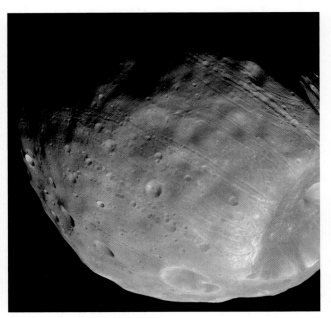

19. Mars's moon Phobos

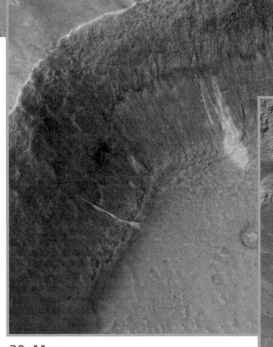

20. Mars

21. Mars

2 km

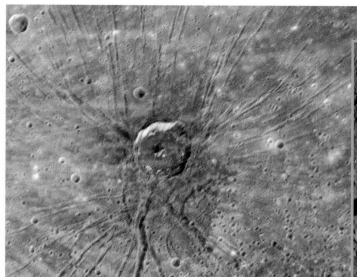

22. Mercury

23. Mercury close-up

24. Venus

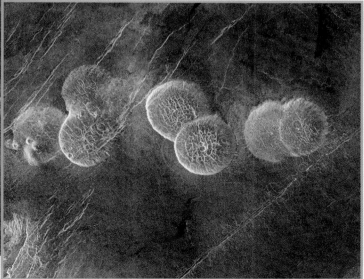

25. Venus close-up

Planet Landforms, Descriptions

1. Jupiter's Moon Europa

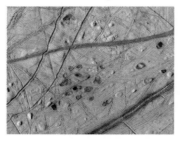

Reddish spots and shallow pits dot the icy surface of Jupiter's moon Europa. These pits might be the result of warm ice bubbling up through the colder icy shell around Europa. Data suggest that a deep liquid-water ocean lies beneath the ice. The red color may be a clue to the composition of the ocean and to whether it could support life.

The fractures and cracks that crisscross the surface also point to a liquid layer below. Water movement cracks the surface, and gaps fill with water and quickly refreeze.

2. Jupiter's Moon Europa

This view of Europa shows a region shaped like a mitten or catcher's mitt. It has a texture that is seen in many parts of Europa's surface. The material in the mitten looks like frozen slush (water). It seems to bulge above the surrounding surface.

Scientists are exploring various hypotheses for the processes that formed these surface textures. These processes include convection, a vertical movement between areas that differ in density due to heating. Other processes could be upwelling of thick icy "lava," and liquid water melting through from an ocean below the surface.

3. Jupiter's Moon Callisto

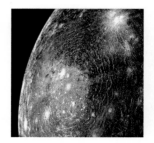

This basin on Jupiter's icy moon Callisto has many rings. It looks like the large impact basins on the surface of Earth's Moon and Mercury. The inner parts of these basins are usually surrounded by ejecta and several mountainous rings. These structures might have formed during an impact. The ring structures on the Moon and Mercury look like ripples produced by a rock thrown into water. The large number of rings observed around this basin is consistent with a low-density layer below the surface. Examination of close-up images suggest that an ocean of liquid water could lie beneath this icy surface.

4. Jupiter's Moon Io

A volcanic eruption on Jupiter's moon Io was captured in this image from February 22, 2000. White and orange areas on the left side of the photo show newly erupted lava. The two small bright spots are exposed molten rock at the edge of lava flows. The larger orange and yellow ribbon is a cooling lava flow that is more than 60 km long. The orange, yellow, and white areas show temperature variations. Orange is the coolest and white the hottest material. Dark deposits surrounding the active lava flows were not there during a November 1999 flyby.

The lava on Io is much hotter than lava produced on Earth. Io is considered to be the most active volcanic body in the solar system because of the amount of thermal energy that its volcanoes produce.

5. Jupiter's Moon Io

This image from October 16, 2001, shows different volcano types on Io. The center shows a large volcanic depression, or  patera, almost 100 km long. It may have formed after eruptions of lava emptied a magma chamber, leaving a space into which the crust collapsed. Evidence of lava flows associated with this patera, however, is scarce. Either the flows were buried, or they never erupted above the surface.

To the right is a shield volcano like the volcanoes in Hawaii. Lava thick enough to pile up into shields is rare on Io. Lava on Io usually runs out in long, thin flows. These lava flows could be made of sulfur.

6–7. Jupiter's Moon Ganymede

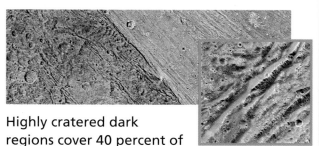

Highly cratered dark regions cover 40 percent of the surface of Ganymede. The remaining 60 percent is covered by a light grooved terrain, which forms intricate patterns. The dark regions are old and rough. They could be the original crust of Ganymede. Lighter regions are young and smooth (unlike Earth's Moon).

Since Ganymede has a low density, it was originally estimated that it is half ice with a rocky core extending to half of its radius. However, a magnetic field around Ganymede strongly indicates that it has a metallic core about 40 to 1,280 km below the surface. The mantle is composed of ice and silicates. The crust is probably a thick layer of ice.

8. Jupiter

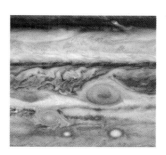

Jupiter's most outstanding surface feature is the Great Red Spot, a swirling mass of gas that looks like a hurricane. The widest diameter of the spot is about three times that of Earth. The color of the spot usually varies from brick-red to slightly brown. Rarely, the spot fades entirely. Its color may be due to small amounts of sulfur and phosphorus in ammonia crystals.

The atmosphere of Jupiter is composed of about 86 percent hydrogen, 14 percent helium, and tiny amounts of methane, ammonia, phosphine, water, acetylene, ethane, germanium, and carbon monoxide. Scientists have calculated these amounts from measurements taken with telescopes and other instruments on Earth and aboard spacecraft. The highest white clouds are made of frozen ammonia crystals. Darker, lower clouds of other chemicals occur in the belts. Astronomers expected to detect water clouds about 70 km below the ammonia clouds. However, none have been discovered at any level.

9. Uranus's Moon Ariel

This high-resolution view of Uranus's icy moon Ariel shows complex crisscrossing valleys with impact craters on top. This narrow-angle view is from a distance of 130,000 km with 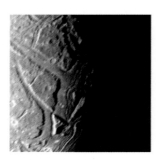 a resolution of about 2.4 km. The faults crossing the valleys are not visible in the bottoms of the valleys they cross. Apparently these valleys filled with deposits sometime after they were formed, leaving them flat and smooth. Trenches later formed, probably by some flow process.

10. Uranus's Moon Miranda

Miranda, the large, icy moon closest to Uranus, is seen at close range in this image, taken January 24, 1986, as part  of a high-resolution mosaic sequence. The narrow-angle view shows an area about 250 km across, at a resolution of about 800 m. Two distinct terrain types are visible: a rugged, higher-elevation terrain (right) and a lower, streaked terrain. Numerous craters on the higher terrain indicate that it is older than the lower terrain. Several slopes, probably faults, cut the different terrains. The impact crater in the lower part of this image is about 25 km across.

11. Saturn

As a gas giant planet, Saturn is mostly atmosphere. The atmosphere is hydrogen and helium, with  traces of ammonia, phosphine, methane, and other compounds. Saturn has powerful lightning storms that are 10,000 times stronger than on Earth. They occur in huge, deep columns nearly as large as Earth. The storms occasionally burst through to the planet's visible cloud tops.

In this image, large swirling storms edge their way along the boundary between cloud bands that flow east-west.

12. Saturn's Moon Titan

This false-color image of Titan shows bodies of liquid near the north pole. These have features that are commonly associated with 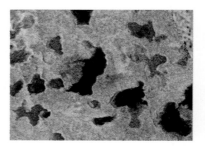 lakes on Earth, such as islands, bays, inlets, and channels. The lakes are most likely liquid methane and ethane.

The lakes on Titan are widespread. At least one lake is larger than Lake Superior on the US/Canadian border. It covers an area of about 100,000 km^2. Analysis of the data indicates that the lakes may be tens of meters deep.

13. Saturn's Moon Enceladus

Enceladus is one of the brightest objects in the solar system. It is covered by ice that reflects sunlight like freshly fallen snow. At least five types of terrain are seen on Enceladus. These include fissures and plains. Crustal deformation indicates that the interior may be liquid.

14–15. Neptune's Moon Triton

A fresh impact crater can be seen in the large, smooth area on the right side of this black-and-white image of Triton. The low cliffs to the left may have been caused by melting surface materials or fluids that flowed in the past.

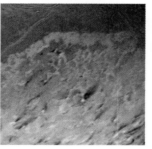

The small white spots in the close-up of Triton appear to be frost around volcanic vents. This false-color image of Triton was taken about 190,000 km from the surface.

16. Neptune

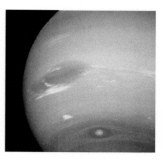

Neptune's atmosphere is like that on the other gas giant planets. It consists mainly of hydrogen and helium with tiny amounts of methane, water, and ammonia. But Neptune has more methane ice in its upper atmosphere, which makes it look blue.

Neptune has a long-lasting storm, called the Great Dark Spot, similar to the Great Red Spot on Jupiter. The fastest winds in the solar system have been clocked on Neptune at 2,400 km per hour. The small white spot below the Great Dark Spot is a bright feature nicknamed Scooter.

17. Neptune

The cloud streaks in this image of the outer atmosphere of Neptune range from 30 to 50 km wide. The white, upper clouds consist mainly of frozen methane. The darker, lower clouds are likely made of hydrogen sulfide. The clouds appear to be approximately 50 km above the surface.

18. Mars

This image shows two Martian volcanoes: Ceraunius Tholus (lower) and Uranius Tholus (upper). Impact craters on the slopes of these volcanoes indicate they are old and inactive. The crater at the summit of Ceraunius Tholus is about 25 km across. Remains of an ancient flow can be seen on the northern slope.

19. Mars's Moon Phobos

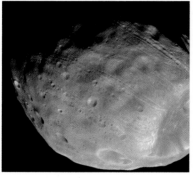

The most striking feature on Phobos, Mars's larger moon, is Stickney crater. It appears in the lower right part of the image. The crater is about 9 km across. Light-colored streaks on the inside of Stickney are landslides. Troughs and crater chains are visible outside the crater. They are probably the result of material ejected from impacts on Mars that flew off and hit Phobos.

20. Mars

Has liquid water flowed on Mars in recent times? This image from June 2000 looks like a water flow on the side of this crater. Since that time, tens of thousands of slopes have been imaged by all the Mars-orbiting spacecraft to see if anything changed. Mars scientists have identified changes.

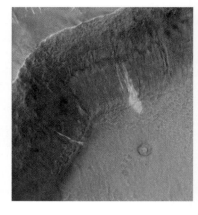

Does this image prove that water recently flowed on Mars? No, but it provides the first evidence of water flow. The surface on Mars is drier than the most arid deserts on Earth. But liquid water from beneath the Martian surface might periodically come to the surface and flow across the planet.

21. Mars

This image shows a fossil delta in Eberswalde crater on Mars. The delta shows the first clear evidence that liquid water flowed on the surface of Mars. This delta is old. The sediments were deposited in water, covered by more sediments, and turned to rock. Wind erosion has exposed this ancient delta.

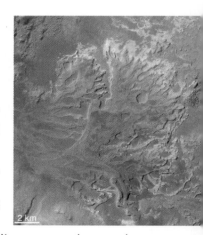

22–23. Mercury

This area on the floor of the Caloris basin (Caloris Planitia) was nicknamed the Spider by the team that studied it. What looks like a set of troughs radiates from the center. The troughs could be evidence that the basin floor broke apart during the impact that formed the crater.

Details of Mercury's surface features are visible in this close-up image. The craters are as small as 400 m. One of the highest cliffs on Mercury sweeps from the top center to the left side of the image. The cliffs must have been formed by tremendous forces in Mercury's crust.

24–25. Venus

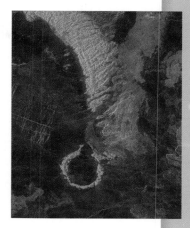

This false-color radar image shows Leda Planitia (plains) of Venus. The oldest rocks are the bright, highly fractured highlands in the upper left. The darker plains that surround the highlands formed when volcanic lava filled the low-lying areas. Plains like this cover as much as 80 percent of the surface of Venus. The most recent lava flows are the bright areas in the upper right. The circular structure in the lower left is probably an impact crater. Venus is struck by meteors at about the same rate as Earth.

In the close-up, seven circular hills dominate the eastern edge of Alpha Regio on Venus. The domes average 25 km in diameter with maximum heights of 750 m. They probably formed when thick lava erupted through the flat plain and flowed outward. These domes might be similar to volcanic domes on Earth. Another suggestion is that the lava pushed up beneath the surface but never erupted onto the plain.

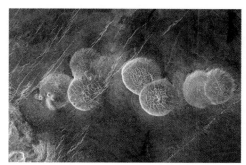

Human Population Growth

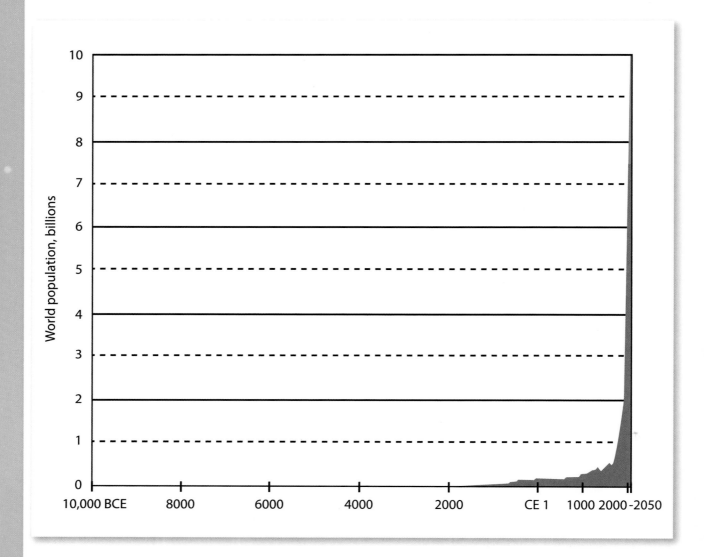

Space Missions

Humans have always looked to the sky and wondered what was out there. Other than a few trips to the Moon, however, we have been unable to visit other worlds. In our place, we send robotic probes.

The National Aeronautics and Space Administration (NASA) has been sending robotic probes into space for about 50 years. These spacecraft collect information far out in the solar system and send it back to Earth. Space probes have parts that work like human senses and abilities.

The table compares the human body to spacecraft counterparts. But it is not completely filled in. Can you name the missing spacecraft parts that function like our body?

Human body	Spacecraft counterpart
Body/torso	The housing holds the spacecraft components and attaches to other devices. Also known as the bus.
Neck	The scan platform turns so that the instruments can point in the desired direction without reorienting the whole spacecraft.
Brain	
Nerves	
Skin	Blankets protect against meteorites and help control temperature. The spacecraft can't sweat, so it uses radiators to get rid of excess heat.
Legs	Rocket motors change a spacecraft's orientation and course.
Blood vessels	
Feet	
Arms	
Sense organs (eyes, ears, nose, taste buds, touch sensors)	
Voice	

Navigation and Orientation

Imagine a spacecraft that has traveled millions of kilometers to fly by a planet. But its cameras are pointed in the wrong direction as it speeds past! People on Earth would be very upset.

To prevent such a disaster, spacecraft use the stars. A probe focuses on the Sun and a bright star, such as Canopus, to navigate and maintain orientation. Small rocket engines keep the probe on course and pointing in the right direction.

Probes communicate with Earth using radio signals. The radio signal is weak if the probe is millions of kilometers from Earth. So NASA ground controllers use a network of huge "ears." These radio antennas are in California, Australia, and Africa. The network listens for the signal and adjusts the antennas for best reception. The signal travels from the "ears" to the probe's crew at a mission-control center.

Spacecraft have many different destinations, instruments, and goals. In its mission to identify planets in the Milky Way that might support life, the Kepler Space Telescope carries the largest camera ever launched into space.

Asteroid Missions

Near Earth Asteroid Rendezvous–Shoemaker

Acronym: NEAR Shoemaker

Destination: 433 Eros

Goals: Collect data on the properties, composition, surface features, interior, and magnetic field of Eros. Study surface properties, interactions with solar wind, possible currents of dust or gas, and asteroid spin. Look for clues about the formation of Earth and other planets.

Launch: February 17, 1996

Arrival: Orbit February 14, 2000; touchdown February 12, 2001

End of Mission: February 28, 2001

Hayabusa

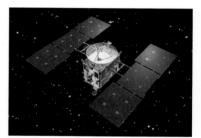

Destination: 25143 Itokawa

Goals: Collect a surface sample of material from the small (550 m by 180 m) asteroid 25143 Itokawa and return the sample to Earth. Record detailed studies of the asteroid's shape, spin, topography, color, composition, density, brightness, interior, and history.

Launch: May 9, 2003

Arrival: September 12, 2005

End of Mission: June 13, 2010

Dawn

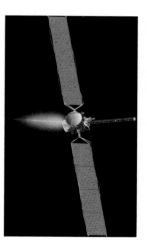

Destination: Vesta and Ceres

Goals: Learn the conditions and processes of the early solar system by detailed investigation of two asteroids. Vesta and Ceres are two of the largest protoplanets not broken up since their formation. Determine how protoplanet size and water content affect the evolution of planets.

Launch: September 27, 2007

Arrival: Vesta orbit 2011–2012; Ceres orbit 2015

End of Mission: Still operating as of 2017

Comet Missions

Stardust

Destination: Comet Wild 2 (pronounced "Vilt 2")

Goals: Collect comet dust during a close encounter with Comet Wild 2. Collect interstellar dust.

Launch: February 7, 1999

Arrival: January 2, 2004

End of Mission: January 15, 2006

Deep Space 1

Acronym: DS1

Destination: Comet Borrelly

Goals: Test 12 new, high-risk technologies. These include ion propulsion (rocket engine using ionized xenon gas), Autonav (automatic navigation system), Remote Agent (remote intelligent self-repair software), Small Deep-Space Transponder (miniaturized radio system and instruments), Solar Concentrator Array, and Beacon Monitor experiment.

Launch: October 24, 1998

Arrival: September 22, 2001

End of Mission: December 18, 2001

Rosetta Orbiter

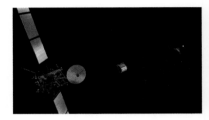

Destination: Comet 67P/Churyumov-Gerasimenko

Goals: Study the origin of comets. Study the relationship between comets and other interstellar material and what this tells us about the origin of the solar system. Describe the comet nucleus, surface features, and composition.

Launch: March 2, 2004

Arrival: May 2014

End of Mission: September 30, 2016

Outer Solar-System Missions

Deep Impact

Destination: Comet Tempel 1

Goals: Investigate the material in comets and whether comets lose their ice or seal it in and become dormant. Study crater formation.

Launch: January 12, 2005

Arrival: July 4, 2005

End of Mission: August 2005

Pioneer 10

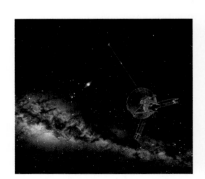

Destination: Jupiter

Goals: Investigate Jupiter system, the constellation Taurus, and beyond.

Launch: March 2, 1972

Arrival: December 3, 1973

End of Mission: March 31, 1997

Pioneer 11

Destination: Jupiter and Saturn

Goals: Investigate Jupiter, Saturn, and the outer solar system. Study energetic particles in the outer solar system (heliosphere).

Launch: April 5, 1973

Arrival: Jupiter 1974; Saturn 1979

End of Mission: September 30, 1995

Juno

Destination: Jupiter

Goals: Build on the results of previous missions and provide new information to help determine how, when, and where Jupiter formed. Collect data from highly elliptical polar orbits (traveling over the north pole to the south pole and back to the north pole) that skim only 5,000 km above the planet's atmosphere. Improve our understanding of the origin of the solar system.

Launch: August 5, 2011

Arrival: July 2016

End of Mission: Still operating as of 2017, planned to end in 2018–19

Voyager 1 and 2

Destination: Jupiter, Saturn, Uranus, and Neptune

Goals: Conduct close-up studies of Jupiter and Saturn, Saturn's rings, and the larger moons of both planets. Voyager 2 was extended to include flybys of Uranus and Neptune. Both Voyagers 1 and 2 will explore the boundaries of our solar system and travel into interstellar space.

Launch: Voyager 2, August 20, 1977; Voyager 1, September 5, 1977

Arrival: Voyager 1: Jupiter 1979; Saturn 1980; outer solar system 2004; entered interstellar space, 2012; Voyager 2: Jupiter 1979; Saturn 1981; Uranus 1986; Neptune 1989; outer solar system 2007

End of Mission: Still operating as of 2017, expected to operate until 2025

Galileo

Destination: Jupiter

Goals: Collect data on the magnetosphere and study Jupiter and its moons. Study Venus, Earth, the Moon, and two asteroids, Gaspra and Ida, during flybys.

Launch: October 18, 1989

Arrival: Probe released July 13, 1995; probe entered atmosphere December 7, 1995

End of Mission: September 21, 2003

Cassini-Huygens

Destination: Saturn

Goals: Conduct a detailed study of Saturn and its moons, including temperature and composition of Saturn's atmosphere, cloud properties, winds, internal structure, rings, icy moons, and Titan.

Launch: October 15, 1997

Arrival: June 30, 2004

End of Mission: Still operating as of 2017, planned to end in September 2017

New Horizons

Destination: Pluto

Goals: Study the dwarf icy planets at the edge of the solar system. Visit Pluto and Charon for the first time. Map surface composition and characterize the geology of Pluto and Charon. Describe the atmosphere of Pluto and search for an atmosphere around Charon. Map surface temperatures on Pluto and Charon. Search for rings and additional moons around Pluto. Conduct similar investigations of one or more Kuiper Belt objects.

Launch: January 19, 2006

Arrival: July 2015

End of Mission: Still operating as of 2017, planned to end in 2019

Mars Missions

Mariner 4

Destination: Mars flyby

Goals: Fly as close as 9,846 km to Mars. Make measurements with various field and particle sensors and detectors, and take images.

Launch: November 28, 1964

Arrival: July 14, 1965

End of Mission: December 21, 1967

Phoenix Mars Lander

Destination: Mars

Goals: Study the history of water in the Martian polar region. Search for evidence of past life in the ice-soil boundary. Analyze the water and soil for evidence of climate cycles and whether the environment could have supported microbial life. Take panoramic, stereoscopic images and close-up images of the soil and water ice from the Martian surface. Describe the geology of Mars, monitor the weather, and investigate properties of the atmosphere and clouds.

Launch: August 4, 2007

Arrival: May 25, 2008

End of Mission: Last communication November 2, 2008; officially ended May 24, 2010

Mars Pathfinder

Destination: Mars

Goals: Demonstrate key engineering technologies and concepts for use in future missions to Mars. Deliver science instruments to the surface of Mars to investigate the structure of the atmosphere, surface meteorology, and surface geology, as well as the form, structure, and elemental composition of rocks and soil.

Launch: December 4, 1996

Arrival: July 4, 1997

End of Mission: September 27, 1997

Mars Global Surveyor

Acronym: MGS

Destination: Mars orbit

Goals: Circle Mars in a polar orbit (traveling over the north pole to the south pole and back to the north pole) once every 2 hours to collect global "snapshots" from 400 km above the Martian surface. Collect data to determine whether life ever existed on Mars, to investigate the character of the climate and geology, and to prepare for human exploration.

Launch: November 7, 1996

Arrival: September 11, 1997

End of Mission: Battery failure and spacecraft lost November 2, 2006; officially ended January 28, 2007

Mars Odyssey

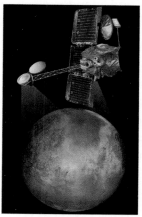

Destination: Mars orbit

Goals: Map the amount and distribution of elements and minerals that make up the Martian surface. Record the radiation environment in low-Mars orbit to determine the radiation-related risk to any future human explorers.

Launch: April 7, 2001

Arrival: October 24, 2001

End of Mission: Still operating as of 2017, expected to operate until 2025

Mars Reconnaissance Orbiter

Acronym: MRO

Destination: Mars orbit

Goals: Search for evidence that water existed on the surface of Mars for a long time. Identify surface minerals. Study how dust and water are transported in the Martian atmosphere.

Launch: August 12, 2005

Arrival: March 10, 2006

End of Mission: Still operating as of 2017

Mariner 9

Destination: Mars orbit

Goals: Transmit images and measure ultraviolet and infrared emissions.

Launch: May 30, 1971

Arrival: November 14, 1971

End of Mission: October 27, 1972

Mars Express

Destination: Mars

Goals: Search for subsurface water from orbit. Study the interaction between solar wind and the atmosphere of Mars. Find out what happened to the large amount of water that was once on Mars.

Launch: June 2, 2003

Arrival: December 26, 2003

End of Mission: Still operating as of 2017

Viking 1 and 2

Destination: Mars

Goals: Obtain high-resolution images of the Martian surface. Characterize the structure and composition of the atmosphere and surface. Search for evidence of life.

Launch: Viking 1, August 20, 1975; Viking 2, September 9, 1975

Arrival: Viking 1 orbiter, June 19, 1976; Viking 1 lander, July 20, 1976; Viking 2 orbiter, August 7, 1976; Viking 2 lander, September 3, 1976

End of Mission: Viking 1 orbiter, August 17, 1980; Viking 1 lander, November 11, 1982; Viking 2 orbiter, June 25, 1978; Viking 2 lander, April 11, 1980

Mars Exploration Rover–Spirit

Acronym: MER

Destination: Mars

Goals: Study rocks and soils that might hold clues to past water activity on Mars.

Launch: June 10, 2003

Arrival: January 4, 2004

End of Mission: Last communication March 22, 2010; officially ended May 25, 2011

Mars Exploration Rover–Opportunity

Acronym: MER

Destination: Mars

Goals: Study rocks and soils that might hold clues to past water activity on Mars.

Launch: July 7, 2003

Arrival: January 25, 2004

End of Mission: Still operating as of 2017

Moon Missions

Lunar Prospector

Destination: Moon

Goals: Look for water ice buried inside the lunar crust and for other natural resources.

Launch: January 7, 1998

Arrival: January 11, 1998

End of Mission: July 31, 1999

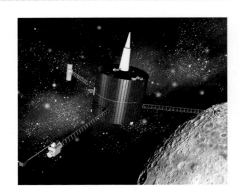

Surveyor

Destination: Moon

Goals: Test midcourse and terminal maneuvers and safely land on the Moon. Test the communications system during cruise, descent, and after landing. Look for locations that would be safe for Apollo landings.

Launch: Surveyors 1 through 7, from May 1966 to January 1968

Arrival: Surveyors 1 through 7, from June 1966 to January 1968

End of Mission: Surveyor 7, February 21, 1968

Ranger 7, 8, and 9

Destination: Moon

Goals: Take high-quality images of the Moon and transmit them back to Earth in real time.

Launch: Ranger 7, July 28, 1964; Ranger 8, February 17, 1965; Ranger 9, March 21, 1965

Arrival: Ranger 7, July 31, 1964; Ranger 8, February 20, 1965; Ranger 9, March 24, 1965

End of Mission: Ranger 7, July 31, 1964; Ranger 8, February 20, 1965; Ranger 9, March 24, 1965

Clementine

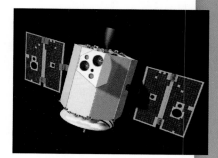

Destination: Moon orbit

Goals: Test lightweight imaging sensors and component technologies for the next generation of Department of Defense spacecraft. Collect data on the Moon and asteroid Geographos.

Launch: January 25, 1994

Arrival: June 1994

End of Mission: June 1994

Apollo

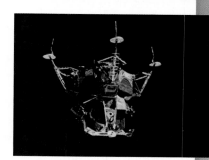

Destination: Moon

Goals: Establish the technology to meet other national interests in space and to achieve preeminence in space for the United States. Explore the Moon and develop human capability to work in the lunar environment.

Launch: Apollo 7, October 11, 1968; Apollo 17, December 7, 1972

Arrival: Apollo 17, December 11, 1972

End of Mission: Apollo 7, October 22, 1968; Apollo 17, December 19, 1972

Lunar Crater Observation and Sensing Satellite

Acronym: LCROSS

Destination: Moon

Goals: Search for water in the form of ice in a crater that is always in shadow at the Moon's south pole. Deploy a device to crash into the crater, creating a plume of potentially icy debris to be measured. Crash itself into the crater, creating a second plume.

Launch: June 18, 2009

Arrival: June 23, 2009

End of Mission: October 9, 2009

Mercury and Venus Missions

Mercury Surface, Space Environment, Geochemistry, and Ranging

Acronym: MESSENGER

Destination: Mercury

Goals: Study the history, origin, and evolution of Mercury. Map nearly the entire planet in color, and image the surface in high resolution. Measure the composition of the surface, atmosphere, and magnetic field.

Launch: August 3, 2004

Arrival: March 18, 2011

End of Mission: April 30, 2015

Mariner 2

Destination: Venus flyby

Goals: Collect data on Venus's atmosphere, magnetic field, charged-particle environment, and mass. Measure the solar wind and interplanetary medium.

Launch: August 27, 1962

Arrival: December 14, 1962

End of Mission: January 3, 1963

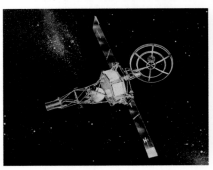

Mariner 5

Destination: Venus flyby

Goals: Measure interplanetary and Venusian magnetic fields, charged particles, plasmas, radio refractivity, and ultraviolet emissions of the atmosphere on Venus.

Launch: June 14, 1967

Arrival: October 19, 1967

End of Mission: November 1967

Mariner 10

Destination: Venus and Mercury flyby

Goals: Measure Mercury's environment, atmosphere, and surface characteristics, and make similar investigations of Venus.

Launch: November 3, 1973

Arrival: Venus flyby, February 5, 1974; Mercury flybys, March 29, 1974; September 21, 1974; March 16, 1975

End of Mission: March 24, 1975

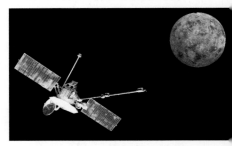

Venus Radar Mapper–Magellan

Destination: Venus orbit

Goals: Make detailed radar images of Venus, map the surface topography, and map the electrical characteristics. Measure Venus's gravitational field and show the planet's internal mass distribution.

Launch: May 4, 1989

Arrival: August 10, 1990

End of Mission: October 11, 1994

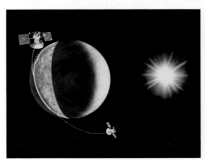

Pioneer Venus

Destination: Venus orbit

Goals: Study the composition of the atmosphere and the characteristics of the upper atmosphere and ionosphere. Investigate solar wind near Venus. Map Venus's surface through a radar-imaging system.

Launch: Orbiter, May 20, 1978; multiprobe, August 8, 1978

Arrival: Orbiter, December 4, 1978; multiprobe, December 9, 1978

End of Mission: October 8, 1992

Sun Missions

Hinode (Solar-B)

Destination: Sun orbit

Goals: Observe the Sun in high-resolution visible light. Observe solar magnetic fields. Investigate the heating mechanism of the solar corona with an X-ray telescope and extreme ultraviolet imaging spectrometer.

Launch: September 22, 2006

End of Mission: Still operating as of 2017

Reuven Ramaty High Energy Solar Spectroscope Imager

Acronym: RHESSI

Destination: Sun orbit

Goals: Investigate the physics of particle acceleration and energy release in solar flares. Observe the processes that take place in the magnetized plasmas of the solar atmosphere during a flare.

Launch: February 5, 2002

End of Mission: Still operating as of 2017

Genesis Solar Wind Sample Return

Destination: Solar wind

Goals: Collect samples of solar wind particles and return them to Earth. Precisely measure the abundance of solar isotopes and elements, and provide a source of solar matter for future scientific analysis. Precisely measure ratios of oxygen, nitrogen, and noble gases in the different phases of solar activity.

Launch: August 8, 2001

End of Mission: September 8, 2004

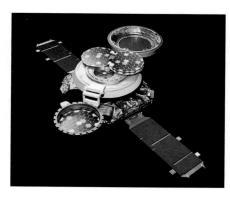

Solar and Heliospheric Observatory

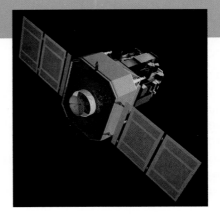

Acronym: SOHO

Destination: Sun orbit

Goals: Determine the structure and dynamics of the solar interior. Investigate the solar corona and the source of its extremely high temperature. Investigate how solar wind is produced.

Launch: December 2, 1995

End of Mission: Still operating as of 2017

Transition Region and Coronal Explorer

Acronym: TRACE

Destination: Sun orbit

Goals: Explore the three-dimensional magnetic structures that emerge through the visible surface of the Sun, the photosphere. Define the dynamics of the upper solar atmosphere, the transition region, and the corona.

Launch: April 1, 1998

End of Mission: June 21, 2010

Solar Terrestrial Relations Observatory

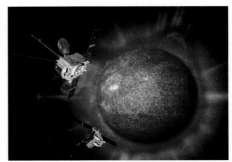

Acronym: STEREO

Destination: Sun orbit

Goals: Trace the flow of energy and matter from the Sun to Earth. Collect data on the three-dimensional structure of coronal mass ejections.

Launch: October 25, 2006

End of Mission: Still operating as of 2017

Solar Dynamics Observatory

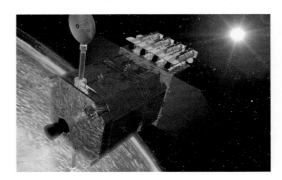

Acronym: SDO

Destination: Sun orbit

Goals: Understand the causes of solar variability and its effect on Earth. Study the Sun's influence on Earth and near-Earth space by observing the solar atmosphere at a small scale in many wavelengths at the same time. Determine how the Sun's magnetic field is generated, structured, and released as energy. Predict solar variations that can affect life on Earth, such as solar flares that can affect cell phones and other technology.

Launch: February 11, 2010

End of Mission: Still operating as of 2017

Space Telescopes

Chandra X-Ray Observatory

Destination: Earth orbit

Goals: Observe X-rays from high-energy regions of the universe, such as the remnants of exploded stars, and active galaxies. Study the origin, evolution, and destiny of the universe.

Launch: July 23, 1999

End of Mission: Still operating as of 2017

Hubble Space Telescope

Acronym: HST

Destination: Earth orbit

Goals: Provide unprecedented deep and clear views of the universe, from the solar system to extremely remote young galaxies.

Launch: April 24, 1990

End of Mission: Still operating as of 2017

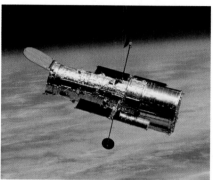

Kepler

Destination: Earth orbit

Goals: Survey our region of the Milky Way galaxy. Detect and characterize Earth-sized and smaller planets where liquid surface water might exist.

Launch: March 6, 2009

End of Mission: Ended prime mission after failure of its reaction wheel 4 on May 11, 2013. New K2 mission uses only two working reaction wheels, and is still operating as of 2017.

Spitzer Space Telescope

Destination: Earth orbit

Goals: Look into regions of space that are hidden from optical telescopes.

Launch: August 25, 2003

End of Mission: Still operating as of 2017

Exoplanet Transit Graphs

A: Kepler 10b

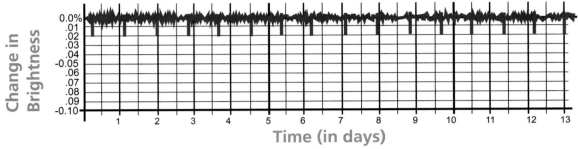

B: HAT-P-7b

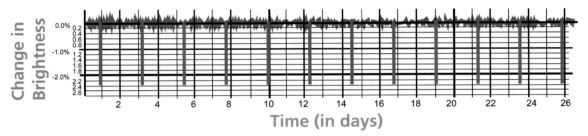

C: Kepler-11e, f, g

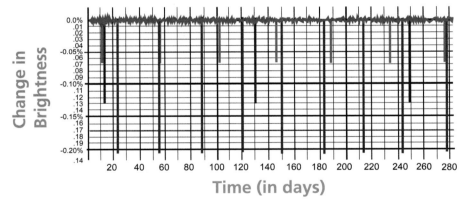

D: Mystery (Hint: there is more than one planet)

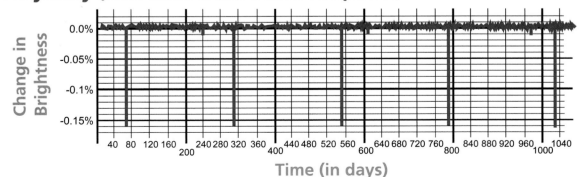

Based on Kepler mission data collected in 2009–2011.

Science Safety Rules

1. Always follow the safety procedures outlined by your teacher. Follow directions, and ask questions if you're unsure of what to do.

2. Never put any material in your mouth. Do not taste any material or chemical unless your teacher specifically tells you to do so.

3. Do not smell any unknown material. If your teacher asks you to smell a material, wave a hand over it to bring the scent toward your nose.

4. Avoid touching your face, mouth, ears, eyes, or nose while working with chemicals, plants, or animals. Tell your teacher if you have any allergies.

5. Always wash your hands with soap and warm water immediately after using chemicals (including common chemicals, such as salt and dyes) and handling natural materials or organisms.

6 Do not mix unknown chemicals just to see what might happen.

7 Always wear safety goggles when working with liquids, chemicals, and sharp or pointed tools. Tell your teacher if you wear contact lenses.

8 Clean up spills immediately. Report all spills, accidents, and injuries to your teacher.

9 Treat animals with respect, caution, and consideration.

10 Never use the mirror of a microscope to reflect direct sunlight. The bright light can cause permanent eye damage.

Science Practices

1. **Asking questions.** Scientists ask questions to guide their investigations. This helps them learn more about how the world works.

2. **Developing and using models.** Scientists develop models to represent how things work and to test their explanations.

3. **Planning and carrying out investigations.** Scientists plan and conduct investigations in the field and in laboratories. Their goal is to collect data that test their explanations.

4. **Analyzing and interpreting data.** Patterns and trends in data are not always obvious. Scientists make tables and graphs. They use statistical analysis to look for patterns.

5. **Using mathematics and computational thinking.** Scientists measure physical properties. They use computation and math to analyze data. They use mathematics to construct simulations, solve equations, and represent different variables.

6. **Constructing explanations.** Scientists construct explanations based on observations and data. An explanation becomes an accepted theory when there are many pieces of evidence to support it.

7. **Engaging in argument from evidence.** Scientists use argumentation to listen to, compare, and evaluate all possible explanations. Then they decide which best explains natural phenomena.

8. **Obtaining, evaluating, and communicating information.** Scientists must be able to communicate clearly. They must evaluate others' ideas. They must convince others to agree with their theories.

Are you a scientist?

Engineering Practices

1. **Defining problems.** Engineers ask questions to make sure they understand problems they are trying to solve. They need to understand the constraints that are placed on their designs.

2. **Developing and using models.** Engineers develop and use models to represent systems they are designing. Then they test their models before building the actual object or structure.

3. **Planning and carrying out investigations.** Engineers plan and conduct investigations. They need to make sure that their designed systems are durable, effective, and efficient.

4. **Analyzing and interpreting data.** Engineers collect and analyze data when they test their designs. They compare different solutions. They use the data to make sure that they match the given criteria and constraints.

5. **Using mathematics and computational thinking.** Engineers measure physical properties. They use computation and math to analyze data. They use mathematics to construct simulations, solve equations, and represent different variables.

6. **Designing solutions.** Engineers find solutions. They propose solutions based on desired function, cost, safety, how good it looks, and meeting legal requirements.

7. **Engaging in argument from evidence.** Engineers use argumentation to listen to, compare, and evaluate all possible ideas and methods to solve a problem.

8. **Obtaining, evaluating, and communicating information.** Engineers must be able to communicate clearly. They must evaluate other's ideas. They must convince others of the merits of their designs.

Are you an engineer?

Engineering Design Process

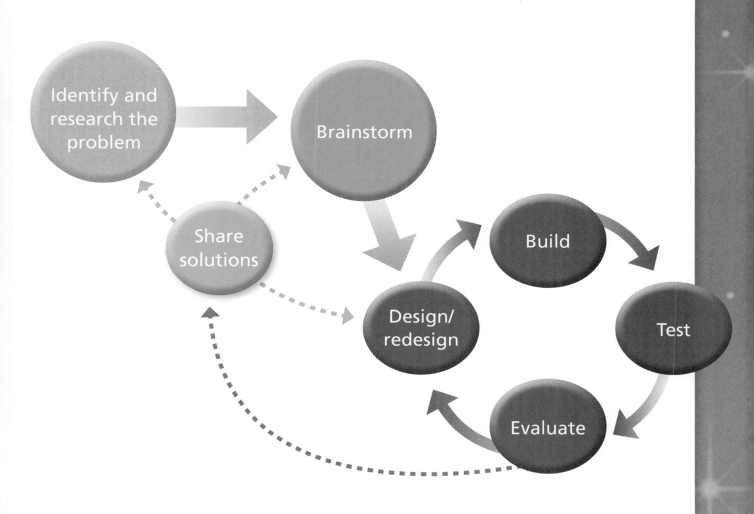

Glossary

absorption line a dark area of a spectrum, indicating the wavelength of absorbed light

anthropocene a new geologic epoch some scientists think we have entered because of human-driven changes

asteroid a small, rocky object that orbits the Sun

asteroid belt a region between Mars and Jupiter that consists of small chunks of matter that orbit the Sun

astronomical unit (AU) the average distance between Earth and the Sun, about 150 million kilometers

atmosphere a layer of gases that surround an object, held in place by gravity

axis an imaginary axle that a planet spins on

barycenter a center of gravity

big bang theory a theory that one explosion created the universe

binary star a system of two stars orbiting their barycenter

biosphere a system of interacting living organisms

bird's-eye view a point of view directly above the area being studied

black hole an extremely dense cosmic object that can form after a star becomes a supernova

circumference the distance around a circle

comet a chunk of ice, dust, and rock material a few kilometers in size

complex crater a crater that has central peaks and ejecta thrown out in long rays

core the center of Earth, made of iron and nickel

cosmos the universe

crater a change in land created by an impact

crescent Moon the shape of the Moon just after and just before the new Moon phase

crust the rigid outer layer of Earth

diameter the distance from one point in a circle to an opposite point in the circle

Doppler shift the shifting of a star's spectrum as it moves

dwarf planet an object that orbits the Sun and is big enough to be round but doesn't clear away all objects near its orbit

ecosystem a community of organisms interacting with each other and with the nonliving environment

ejecta the material displaced from the land when a crater is formed

electromagnetic spectrum the range of electromagnetic radiation arranged in order of energy level

emission line a bright line of a spectrum, indicating the wavelength of emitted light

emit to give off

equator the imaginary line that runs around the middle of a planet, halfway between the North and South Poles

equinox a day of the year when the Sun's rays shine straight down on the equator

exoplanet a planet orbiting a star other than the Sun

first-quarter Moon the phase that occurs halfway between the new and full Moon

flooded crater a crater from a large impact that filled with magma from beneath the surface

fossil fuel the remains of organisms that lived long ago preserved as oil, coal, or natural gas

fracking a type of technology that injects liquids into the ground to force oil out

frame of reference the assemblage of objects, distances, and directions that you use to establish the location of something

full Moon the phase of the Moon that occurs when the Moon is opposite the Sun as seen from Earth

galaxy an enormous collection of tens of millions to hundreds of billions of stars, interstellar gas, and dust

geosphere Earth's core, mantle, and crust

gibbous a Moon shape that is larger than a first or third quarter Moon, but smaller than a full Moon

gravity a force of attraction between masses

greenhouse gas a gas that absorbs and radiates energy in the atmosphere, trapping thermal energy and heating the atmosphere

highlands light-colored areas of the Moon with lots of rough mountains and craters

hydrosphere the interacting water on, under, and above Earth's surface

impact the crash between one object (impactor) and another object

interacting to act upon one another

Kuiper (KI•per) Belt the region of the solar system beyond the orbit of Neptune; plutoids are located here

latitude the angular distance north or south from Earth's equator

light-year (ly) the distance light travels in 1 year. One ly is about equal to 9.5 trillion kilometers.

Local Group a relatively small cluster of several dozen galaxies, including the Milky Way

location the position of an object relative to other objects

lunar pertaining to the Moon

lunar eclipse when Earth is exactly between the Moon and the Sun, and the Moon passes through Earth's shadow

Magellanic Clouds the galaxies closest to the Milky Way

mantle the layer of Earth below the crust; upper part is solid and lower part is semisolid

mare (plural **maria**) the dark surface of cooled magma in a flooded crater

meteor a streak of light in the sky from gravel- and pebble-sized meteoroids; also known as a shooting star

meteorite a piece of a meteoroid that hits the ground

meteoroid a small- or medium-sized piece of rock or metal from space

Milky Way the name of the galaxy that our solar system is a part of

model a representation of thinking to help others understand your thinking

Moon Earth's natural satellite

nebula (plural **nebulae**) a cloud of gas and dust in space between stars

new Moon the phase of the Moon that occurs when the Moon is in the direction of the Sun as seen from Earth

nonrenewable a material that cannot be replaced once used up

North Star the reference star pointed to by Earth's North Pole

Oort Cloud an area of icy planetesimals in the outer solar system past the planets

orbit the path one object takes to travel around another object (synonym: revolution)

orbital period how long it takes an object to orbit another object

orbital radius the average distance between an object and the object it is orbiting

parallel continuing in the same direction and always the same distance apart

phase each different shape of the Moon

planet an object that orbits a star and is massive enough for its own gravity to force it into a spherical shape

planetesimal a piece of material from the collision of planets

plutoid a type of dwarf planet that has an orbit beyond Neptune

radiometer an instrument that detects microwave emissions

ray the white lines that extend in all directions from some craters

red giant the stage of a star when it becomes very large and has a relatively cool surface

renewable able to be replaced or restored by nature

revolution the path one object takes to travel around another object (synonym: orbit)

rotation spinning on an axis

satellite an object orbiting a larger object

season a period of the year identified by changes in hours of daylight and weather

simple crater a small, bowl-shaped crater that has a fairly uniform blanket of ejecta distributed around the rim

solar pertaining to the Sun

solar eclipse when the Moon passes exactly between Earth and the Sun

solar energy energy from the Sun

solar system a region of space occupied by a system of objects orbiting a star, such as the Sun and all things orbiting it

solstice a day of the year when Earth's North Pole is leaning either toward the Sun or away from the Sun

spectroscope a tool used to study the spectrum of colors coming from a light source

spectrum a pattern of wavelengths that can identify different kinds of light

star a large, hot ball of gas

star cluster a group of stars held together by their mutual gravitational attraction

subsystem a system that also makes up part of a larger system

Sun the star at the center of our solar system

supernova an explosion that ends a star's life

system a collection of interacting parts

third-quarter Moon the phase that occurs halfway between the full and new Moon

transit when one object appears to move across another object as seen from the perspective of an observer

universe the sum total of all things that can be observed or detected

visible light wavelengths of electromagnetic radiation that can be seen by the human eye

waning getting smaller

wavelength the length of one wave cycle

waxing getting bigger

white dwarf the stage of a star when it has no more fuel for nuclear reactions

wobble method a method to detect a possible planet by studying the spectrum lines of stars

Index